SAFETY AFLOAT
UNDER SAIL AND POWER

Safety Afloat

UNDER SAIL AND POWER

A HANDBOOK BY
W. ZANTVOORT

TRANSLATED FROM THE DUTCH BY
J. DE REUS AND ADRIAN HEAD

HOLLIS & CARTER
LONDON

PUBLISHER'S NOTE

For the convenience of British yachtsmen the Continental metrical measurements have been supplemented, in the tables, by British measurements given in round figures. Our thanks are due to Mr. B. Thompson for converting the measurements and for valuable work on the tables.

Originally published by C. A. J. van Dishoeck,
Bussum, as *Behouden Vaart*
English translation © Hollis & Carter 1964
Printed and bound in Great Britain for
Hollis & Carter Ltd
by Cox & Wyman Ltd, Fakenham
Set in Monotype Plantin
First published in Great Britain 1964

CONTENTS

FOREWORD

'Fearless be he who travelling forth would fare
But watchful, and of dangers full aware,'

so says an old proverb. But *watching* for danger is, alas! only half the story.

When investigating the causes of damage in yachts I have again and again found that the safety precautions on board leave much to be desired. The equipment is frequently inadequate; and in many vessels engine and cooking-gas installations are unsuitable, in some even positively dangerous. This is not the result so much of pig-headedness as of ignorance.

I have tried in the light of experience to collect together the guiding principles for furthering safety on board. Although it is highly improbable that anyone will immediately put all the recommendations of this book into practice, it is certainly possible to make a beginning with the suggestions from some of the following chapters in the interests of a safe passage.

I would like to acknowledge my gratitude to Adrian Head for his invaluable assistance in preparing the English version of this book. But for him and his *botter* '*Johanna*' this edition would not have been published.

W.Z.

I. How to Buy and Inspect a Yacht

WHEN BUYING a yacht the prospective owner who has some experience with boats can get a fair idea of the vessel just by keeping his eyes open. The appearance and the standard of maintenance of a ship say a great deal about the care that has been bestowed on it. For a proper inspection a boat must be slipped, since most defects are to be found below the water-line. The places that deserve special notice are those where water or dirt can accumulate. This applies as much to steel as to wooden boats. Faults may also be expected behind fixed panelling and under fixed cabin soles. The condition of the propeller-shaft, the clearance between shaft and stern-tube, and the play in the rudder hangings should be inspected carefully.

One must pay close attention to the seams of a wooden ship. These seams should not be too wide and should not be frayed. The seams of a ship that has begun to work owing to too light construction or age must be caulked frequently. The edges of the strakes become damaged and the wood is crushed: decay starts at these points and leaks will occur when under way. At stem and stern special attention should be paid to the seams, to the fastening of the planking to the stem and to the stern-post or to the transom, as also to the abutments of the different sections of the stern, deadwood, etc. Inboard, the step of the mast requires close inspection, while the fastening of the planking to the frames and of the floors to the keel should also be carefully checked. Leaks in the deck and superstructure are always betrayed by discolorations down the interior woodwork. Such leaks are often very difficult to remedy and are frequently the cause of decay in deck-beams and other members.

Steel yachts are first inspected by tapping with a hammer. In this way an experienced ear can gain an impression of the relative thicknesses of the shell plates. If one finds a spot that sounds thin, a hole should be drilled and the thickness of the plate measured with a gauge. It is thus possible to determine how much of the thickness of the plate has been lost. A decrease of up to thirty per cent is still acceptable for yachts.

Outboard, one should look for severe local corrosion and missing rivet-heads. Inboard, the same holds good as for wooden ships. All parts should be carefully finished; for example, flanges of frames and beams should be a snug fit against the plating. All unions should be a tight fit. The presence of concrete in a steel hull is not necessarily a sign of age. It is wise, however, to make sure that in those places the plating is still tight up against the concrete. This can be done by knocking on the outside (hammer testing). As soon as rust is present between plating and concrete, the concrete must be chipped out and renewed, and the thickness of the plating determined. It is hardly ever possible effectively to inhibit the development of rust marks once they have begun to appear on the hull plates from behind wales or fittings riveted to the hull. Painting, in this case, solves the problem for a few months only.

The other parts of a yacht which should satisfy certain special requirements will be discussed in more detail in later chapters.

RIGGING

Naturally the condition of the sails is easy to assess, since they will seldom develop latent defects. The fastening of the cloth to the bolt-ropes, and the condition of the cloth itself, should be carefully examined. The strength of cotton canvas can be determined as follows: fold it along the thread, take it between the thumb and fore-finger of both hands and try to tear it; good-quality sailcloth will not tear in this test. (Fig. 1.)

Wooden spars should be inspected for dark discolorations, especially where fittings are attached to the mast, and for defects in glued seams. Both are bad omens: in the case of dark discoloration rot is approaching or has already set in, while a glued seam that has come loose will loosen further and can never be adequately repaired.

Aluminium spars should be carefully checked for slack rivets in fittings and signs of corrosion.

Fig. 1

Galvanized steel wire which is rusty should be rejected. Bright steel wire should be laid open with a marline spike, in order to check whether rust has formed between the strands. As soon as rust is present in any degree steel wire cannot be trusted any longer.

THE ENGINE

Unless the engine is dismantled, it is difficult to get a complete picture of its condition. A good, clear running note, easy starting and smoke-free exhaust are indicative of good condition; in addition there should be no, or hardly any, oil consumption. An expert inspection will give one a very good idea of its condition. If one does not want such an inspection, it is advisable to demand a written guarantee that the seller will pay for any wear-and-tear defects which may subsequently come to light within a given period; but if the seller is unwilling to honour his guarantee, its enforcement, in Great Britain, is likely to be a lengthy and expensive process. With the aid of the engine number the manufacturer or dealer will be able to provide useful information concerning the year of manufacture and the engine's past history. In addition it is advisable to make sure that spare parts are still commercially available for the particular type of engine under consideration.

EQUIPMENT

Inspection of the equipment of the ship, such as anchors, chains, navigation lights and so on, presents no difficulty, so long as it is remembered that they should appear to be in reasonable order and should be usable. This applies also to the purchase of open boats. These boats are much simpler, however, so one can get a very good all-round impression of them in a shorter time.

The most difficult point when purchasing a yacht is the question whether the price to be paid is in accordance with the value of the ship and the defects found, and, moreover, whether the defects can be tolerated or whether immediate repair is necessary. The conclusion will usually be reached that it would be best to obtain the services of a professional surveyor.

The owner of a yacht must decide for himself whether he wants to risk his life; but he owes a duty to his guests and to his crew to take all measures necessary to ensure their safety. In Britain this obligation on the owner of a vessel was reformulated by the Occupier's Liability Act, 1957.

Extremely useful publications furthering the good construction and maintenance of yachts can be obtained from Lloyd's Register of Shipping, 71 Fenchurch Street, London, E.C.3. Advice on surveys can also be obtained from this address.

II. Prevention of Fire and Explosion

ONE OF the greatest hazards faced by the crew of a yacht is that of fire and explosion. Every year serious accidents occur which could have been prevented if engine and gas installations had been in good order.

Contrary to the general belief, petrol in its liquid state does not burn. It is the petrol vapour mixed with air which is highly inflammable. The vapour of a teacup full of petrol mixed with the proper amount of air has an explosive power of 4–6 lb. TNT.

Petrol vapour, propane, butane and similar gases are heavier than air and therefore collect in the bilges. An explosive mixture can remain there for a long time if the yacht is not properly ventilated. The main object, however, is to prevent explosive mixtures from collecting in the bilges and to keep fire, mainly in the form of sparks from the electrical installations, away from any gas mixtures. As a marine surveyor the writer has investigated numerous cases of fire and explosion and from the lessons learned has compiled the following recommendations:

FUEL TANK

The tank should preferably be installed in an accessible place so that it may easily be removed for cleaning. The tank should be securely fitted as far from the engine and exhaust and as low as possible. For engines with a gravity-feed carburettor the tank has to be at least 1 ft. above the carburettor. The tank should be made of a suitable material such as stainless steel, galvanized steel or fibreglass or, in case of diesel oil, normal plate steel. Fuel tanks of more than 8 gallons should be fitted with baffle-plates. The tank should be subjected to a test pressure of 8 ft. of water. This can be done by fitting an 8-ft. pipe on the filling pipe of the tank and filling the tank and pipe with water. The level of the water gives a clear indication whether there is a leak.

The fuel feed pipe should be connected to a strong and suitable leak-proof stopcock which is fitted directly to the tank. This stopcock should be in an easily accessible position or should be fitted with a transmission in order to open and close the tap from on deck. Installations with fuel pumps can simply have a pipe leading through the top of the tank, but if in this case the tank is higher than the engine, a stopcock should be fitted as well because the fuel pipe will act as a siphon.

It is desirable to have a sump in the bottom of the tank in which sludge and water can collect and which can be drained by a separate tap. The fuel feed pipe to the motor should reach down into the tank to a point *no lower* than 2 in. above the bottom of this sump so that water and dirt will not be drawn up. (Fig. 2A.)

The piping between tank and deck should be completely tight so that no fuel or vapour can leak into the hull. The filler cap should be fitted on deck outside the superstructure and nowhere near any openings or scuttles so that, when the tank is filled, no petrol or vapour will get inboard. The filler pipe should extend into the tank to 2 in. above the bottom to effect a vapour seal whilst filling. The cap of the filler should be marked 'petrol' or 'diesel'. This cap should preferably be fitted above the level of the deck in order to keep the tank as free as possible from rain water or spray which might otherwise penetrate under the cap. (Fig. 2B.) A vent pipe should be fitted to the tank, the end of the vent pipe to be led well away from all openings leading to the inside of the ship. The end should be covered with fine-mesh copper gauze.

Petrol tanks may not be fitted with a gauge; diesel fuel tank gauges should have self-closing cocks fitted directly on the tank if a gauge is fitted.

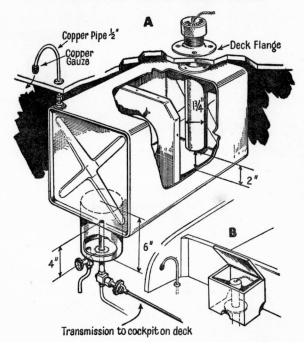

Fig. 2

FUEL PIPING

The fuel pipe should be made of annealed copper pipe with brazed or 'metal-to-metal' joints. The pipe should be secured with clips, spaced not more than 1 ft. apart so that vibration is prevented.

Between the fixed pipe and the engine an expansion loop should be made or, in case of a rubber-mounted engine, a flexible connection should be fitted. In the latter case, both engine and tank should be properly earthed in order to prevent a static load building up. Copper pipe with expansion loops should be annealed annually. All connections should be 'metal-to-metal'.

A fuel filter with a stopcock between the filter and the line to the tank is desirable and for diesel fuel essential. (Fig. 3.) The cocks

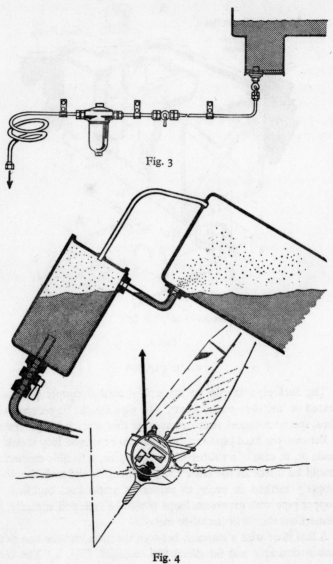

Fig. 3

Fig. 4

should be of the non-leak variety which unfortunately cost more than the ordinary ones. Normal cocks, however, are not completely leak-proof for long. The pipe should be laid as directly and as straight as possible from the tank to the engine; big loops tend to collect water or gas which may stop the engine.

Diesel installations should be fitted so that even the rolling of the vessel will not allow air into the fuel pipes. (Fig. 4.) If air gets into the fuel system of a diesel engine it will stop, and then the whole system has to be made air-free before the engine can be started again.

THE CARBURETTOR

A suitable filter or flame-arrester should be fitted to the air intake of all carburettors. Under all carburettors, except those of a down-draught type, a driptray screened on the upper side with fine copper-wire mesh should be fitted so that petrol in the tray cannot ignite. Between tray and carburettor a pipe can be fitted which will ensure that the vapour of the petrol, collected in the tray, is drawn off into the engine. (Fig. 5.)

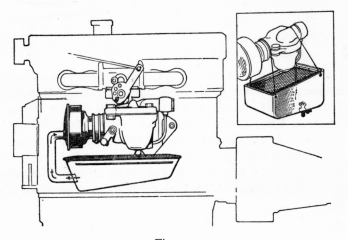

Fig. 5

B

EXHAUST PIPES

A poorly fitted exhaust pipe may greatly reduce the output of the engine and may cause excessive carbon deposits. A copper exhaust pipe of suitable diameter is desirable for petrol engines because steel pipes will corrode rapidly; for diesel engines which have less corrosive exhaust-gases steel will do as well.

A suitable silencer is essential. The dry type does not cause any condensation but gets very hot and requires very efficient lagging.

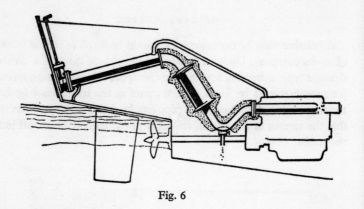

Fig. 6

One layer of asbestos cord is entirely insufficient. A water-cooled exhaust pipe and silencer suppresses noise more effectively and cools more efficiently but collects condensation and is more subject to corrosion. A water-cooled exhaust should be lead for this reason so that no condensation can run back into the engine. The same applies to an exhaust into which cooling water is injected. A valve at the outer end of the exhaust pipe is necessary especially for sailing yachts whose engines are not normally in constant use at sea. (Fig. 6.)

ENGINE-ROOM VENTILATION
(see also Chapter VI)

Good ventilation is of paramount importance. A natural-draught ventilation system can be made by fitting two cowls, one heading forward and one aft. The one heading forward should be situated at the aft end of the compartment to be ventilated, the one heading aft at the forward end because all vessels tend to ventilate from aft forward when heading into the wind. Petrol engine installations should be fitted with a spark-proof extractor with the suction leading from the lowest point in the engine-room and the outlet led overboard as far away as possible from scuttles, companionways and hatches. The blower should be switched on and off by a combined

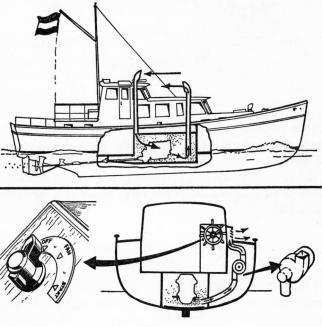

Fig. 7

blower and ignition switch, which will start the blower before the ignition is switched on. (Fig. 7.)

DRIPTRAY

In wooden yachts a metal tray longer and wider than the engine should be fitted between the engine bearers in order to prevent contamination of the bilges by oil and fuel leaking from the engine.

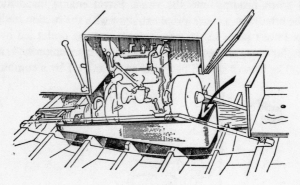

Fig. 8

In steel yachts a water-tight bulkhead at the forward end of the engine compartment, or in bigger yachts forward and aft of the engine-room, will be sufficient.

The tray under the engine should be big enough to allow any object (nuts, spanners, etc.) which may fall into it to be recovered easily. (Fig. 8.)

ELECTRICAL INSTALLATION
(Engine-room)

The electrical installation in the engine-room should be absolutely spark proof. All cables should be of the marine type properly secured to cable-ways, to prevent damage by vibration or heat. (See Chapter V.)

SOME GENERAL OBSERVATIONS
ON SAFETY PRECAUTIONS

The following points are of importance on board all kinds of yachts and ought to form part of the standard daily routine when the tank is filled:

1. All electric equipment to be stopped and any gas turned off and openings such as doors, scuttles, etc., to be closed. Open fires and paraffin stoves to be extinguished. No smoking!

2. The nozzle of the fuel filling hose to be brought in contact with the filler pipe before filling is commenced, to avoid static sparks.

3. Tank and piping to be checked for leaks.

4. Engine-room to be ventilated before restarting of the engine for at least five minutes (very important).

5. No electrical equipment to be started, or open fire, gas or paraffin to be used before all smell of petrol has disappeared.

6. A suitable fire-extinguisher to be held ready during the whole procedure.

Furthermore for general safety it is strongly urged that it should be a rule to:

(a) Close fuel taps when the engine is not in use.

(b) Keep the engine-room as clean as possible.

(c) Use approved type cans for spare fuel only if no other arrangements can be made. The cans should be stowed upright in a cool and well-ventilated place. Some polyester cans are dangerous because they are not fit to contain fuel for a long period and may collect static electricity. Metal cans should be prevented from rubbing against each other and against other metal with some inert packing. As far as possible any movement should be prevented. Foam rubber off-cuts are a suitable material. Absorbent materials such as cotton waste should be avoided.

Petrol, as we have mentioned, will evaporate as soon as it appears, even at very small leaks. A slight discolouring will give an indication of the location of a leak. All leaks should be repaired immediately. A slight leak is an ideal generator of explosive vapour. Cabin-cruisers and auxiliary sailing yachts should have hatches or emergency hatches providing a usable second exit from all the accommodation. These hatches should have locks which can always be opened from the inside.

FIRE DANGERS FROM GALLEY STOVES

Defects in bottled gas installations regularly cause serious explosions, and paraffin and spirit cookers are also a potential source of danger. All stoves and cookers should be properly secured so that they cannot accidentally be overturned.

Butane and propane, both liquid petroleum gases,[1] are widely used for cooking and heating. Gas is very practical but also very dangerous. It is heavier than air and for this reason a leak will fill up the boat with gas in the same way as a liquid would. One can walk waist-deep in petroleum gas without smelling it unless the gas is stirred up to nose level. The danger of bottled gas lies in the fact that there is always an explosive layer on top of the gas. A flame or a spark in this layer will always cause an explosion setting off the remainder of the gas. The explosion will never be followed by a fire unless open petrol or similar liquids are ignited.

In most countries the use of butane and propane on board commercial vessels has been brought under government supervision; regulations for these installations are very strict and complicated.[2] Not all legal requirements can be fulfilled in smaller yachts, but the following recommendations can and should be followed. (Fig. 9.)

1. Propane and butane should normally only be used as fuel for stoves, water-heaters and refrigerators.

[1] These are sold under various trade names but the remarks in this section apply to all gases used for cooking in boats.

[2] There are no regulations applying to yachts in England as yet (1964) where used by the owner for pleasure. Stringent regulations apply to the carriage of passengers for reward in all but the smallest boats. Any hirer of craft is liable to his charterers if the craft is not safe. Equally an owner would be liable to his guests for an accident due to his want of proper care. (Occupier's Liability Act, 1957.)

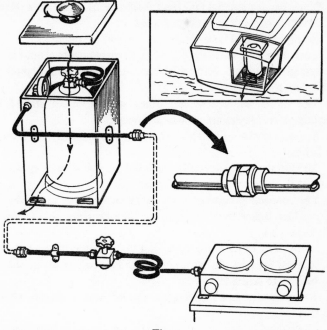

Fig. 9

2. No part of the gas installation should be in the engine-room.

3. The gas-cylinder and reducing valve should be placed on deck in a properly ventilated box or in a steel box built into the hull with ventilation openings to the outside. No electrical wiring should lead through the box nor should tools or gear be stowed in the box.

4. Gas-cylinders should be properly secured and stowed upright.

5. The reducing valve should be suitable for the gas used and rigidly mounted either to the box or to the cylinder. The pressure in the gas pipe should lie between 5·5 and 12·5 oz. per in.^{2}.

6. The connection between cylinder and stove should be made of seamless steel or copper pipe $\frac{1}{4}$ in. minimum internal diameter. The entire drop of pressure in the pipeline should not be more than 1 oz. per in.^{2}.

7. A pipe passing a metal bulkhead should be laid through a special bulkhead fitting secured to the bulkhead.

8. The piping should have expansion loops where required.

9. Joints should be minimized but where unavoidable should be in an accessible position. Preferably 'metal-to-metal' joints should be used. (Fig. 9.)

10. The piping in lockers and other storage places should be properly protected against accidental damage.

11. A main tap should be fitted where the piping enters the accommodation.

12. All taps should be specially made for gas and of such construction that they cannot be opened accidentally.

13. The connection between pressure-reducing valve and piping in the cylinder locker may be approved high-pressure hose, secured with hose clips.

14. Stoves and other equipment should be properly secured and the adjacent area should be fireproofed. The compartment should also be easy to ventilate.

15. Water-heaters and refrigerators should have a thermo-safety-valve.

16. The following instructions should be fitted near the installation in an obvious place:

(a) do not light matches before compartment is properly ventilated;

(b) close valve on cylinder when installation is not in use;

(c) use soapy water to detect leaks, never use a naked flame.

17. Once every four years the installation should be subjected to a test pressure of 4 lb. per in.^{2}. This pressure should be maintained without pumping for fifteen minutes.

The above recommendations are sometimes impossible to follow on board small sailing yachts, where there is no space available on deck for a properly ventilated box and the space under the cockpit seats cannot be ventilated properly. In this case the best solution is a burner which is mounted directly on the gas-cylinder.

A very easy and very efficient method of checking the tightness of the system is prescribed by the U.S. Coast Guard regulations. They recommend fitting a manometer with a working range of 0–16 oz. per in.[2] on the low-pressure pipeline. When the valve on the cylinder is opened the manometer will immediately indicate the pressure in the pipeline. When the valve on the cylinder is closed again the manometer must remain on the same indication for at least fifteen minutes. If the manometer slowly runs down one can be certain that there is a leak which must be detected with soapy water. It is wise to check for leaks in this way every time one comes on board for a week-end or a cruise.

All these recommendations may seem rather complicated but in practice they are fairly simple. A little forethought and a little work is infinitely more agreeable than being blown overboard by an explosion!

FIRE-EXTINGUISHERS

Every yacht fitted with an engine and/or galley equipment should carry at least one suitable fire-extinguisher of ample capacity. Many and widely varying types of extinguishers are available to yachtsmen, but not all are equally suitable. For engine-room and engine fires, dry-powder, CO_2 or foam extinguishers should be used. Galley fires can best be fought with CO_2 extinguishers because the snow completely evaporates and does not contaminate the food. CO_2 extinguishers, however, are slightly less effective than dry-powder or foam. Smouldering mattresses or wood are very difficult to extinguish; for these materials water will have to be used to finish the job.

Methyl bromide extinguishers should not be used on board and C.T.C. and chloro-bromo-methane extinguishers should never be used in confined spaces because the vapour may be dangerous under certain conditions. The prices of good extinguishers are fairly high but the price of a fire which cannot be fought will always be higher.

The siting of the extinguishers has to be considered carefully and has to be such that one can always be reached under all circumstances.

For bigger yachts, especially motor-yachts, a built-in CO_2

installation for the engine-room is highly desirable. This installation can be made fully automatic or capable of being operated from the bridge.

Fire-extinguishers should be inspected by the manufacturer at the prescribed time. A little experience in the use of the extinguishers can do no harm. For this reason in autumn, when all gear is taken home, old rags soaked in fuel may be set on fire and extinguished for practice.

Although a petrol or paraffin fire can in general be fought only with CO_2, powder or foam, a bucket of water under favourable circumstances may extinguish the beginning of a petrol fire merely by cooling the whole of the area to below flash point.

III. Inboard Engine Installation

WITH MANY yachts, even motor-yachts, the engine installation is all too often considered a matter of secondary importance. Often the engine is mounted in such a way that it is difficult of access; frequently it is poorly installed, which reduces its reliability and involves a greater risk of fire.

The engine-bed is the basis of a good installation. Hence the bearers should be sufficiently strong and firmly secured to the boat. It is important that the engine be carefully aligned and stay aligned when in use. This is impossible if the bearers are not sufficiently rigid; excessive wear and tear and a leaking stern-tube will be the inevitable consequences. The bearers should be as long as possible and be well fixed to the frames or floors; strong bearers reduce the chance of undesirable vibrations and deaden the sound of the engine.

FLEXIBLE MOUNTING

In some boats the sound of the engine is definitely annoying. Part of this sound is transmitted to the hull via the engine-bed. If there is sufficient room the engine can be placed on flexible mountings in order to eliminate this sound transmission. It should be borne in mind, however, that the connection between engine and propeller-shaft should in that case also be flexible, as well as all the other connections between boat and engine, such as water pipes, oil pipes and electric wiring. For small engines flexible couplings exist that take up the thrust of the shaft. (Fig. 10.) With large engines a special thrust-block between the flexible coupling and the stern-tube has to be mounted on the shaft. With diesel engines special precautions should be taken so that no diesel oil can leak on to the flexible mountings. Although the rubber of the mountings is usually claimed to be oil-resistant, it is nevertheless often attacked by diesel

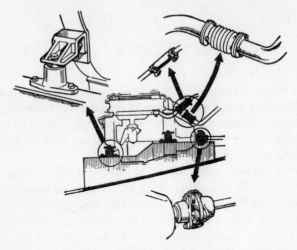

Fig. 10

oil. The advice of the supplier or the manufacturer of the engine
should always be obtained as to the dimensions and type of flexible
mountings to be used.

For sound insulation good results may be obtained from glass
wool, which is fastened to the bulkheads and to the underside of the
deck in the engine compartment behind perforated galvanized iron
or aluminium sheets. As a source of undesirable sound the exhaust
should not be forgotten. The sound transmitted by the exhaust pipe
is reduced by insulation or by a water-jacket. Very good results are
generally achieved with a water-cooled water-injection silencer
placed close to the engine.* (Fig. 11.)

ALIGNMENT

(Placing the engine in the correct position in relation to the propeller-shaft.)

An engine which is rigidly mounted on to the bearers must be
aligned very carefully. This is done as follows: the bolts of all flange

*See page 18 on the installation of these silencers.

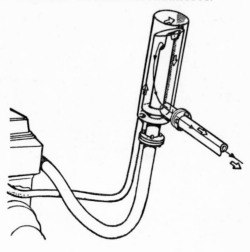

Fig. 11

couplings in the shaft line are loosened. Beginning with the propeller-shaft each set of flanges is pushed a little asunder, after which a
feeler gauge is used to check whether the distance between the faces
is the same everywhere. If this is so, the flanges are bolted together.
At the next coupling this procedure is repeated. Should the shaft or
the engine appear not to be in line, the shaft or engine must be
moved as required. A prerequisite of this method of alignment is
that the shaft be straight and that the flanges be at right angles to the
shaft. Alignment of a propeller-shaft should always be done when the
boat is afloat and the hull has assumed its waterborne shape.
(Fig. 12.)

Sometimes installations are found in which one or two universal
joints have been fitted in the shaft. These universal joints are not
ideal, because they cause extra wear and tear, involve extra cost and
offer extra resistance. For a small engine in a confined space, however, a universal joint may sometimes be the only practical solution.
In that case particular care should be taken to see that the universal
joints are sufficiently strong to transmit the engine power to the propeller. The strength is determined on the basis of the power of the

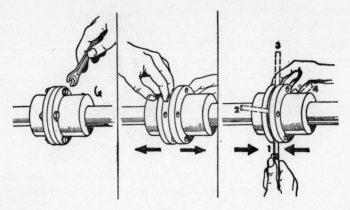

Fig. 12

engine and the number of revolutions per minute of the shaft; the supplier of the joint can advise about this. An old universal joint from a motor-car, bought from a breaker's yard, is certainly not a good solution. Special universal joints, if required with shafts, are commercially available.

STERN-TUBE

The propeller-shaft in the stern-tube is usually supported in two places; viz. at the inside in the gland and at the outside in a bearing made of nylon, rubber, white metal, bronze or cast iron. A rubber bearing is lubricated by the water that flows along the ship; hence care should be taken that the water can easily reach the inlets provided for this purpose and that these inlets are open. A rubber bearing that is not sufficiently lubricated or fits too tightly will wear very rapidly. If the bearing is dry while the ship is slipped, the propeller-shaft must not be turned at all. Metal bearings can be lubricated with grease, a soft type of grease being the best for this purpose. To lubricate the tail-shaft a special grease-gun with a line to the stern-tube should be mounted. This grease-gun should be easily accessible, preferably in a position where no hatch covers need to be removed for access, and should not be too small. The line between grease-gun and stern-tube should have a diameter large enough for the grease to be easily forced through, even when cold.

In the last few years all sorts of special combined propulsive and steering units (stern drives) have appeared on the market, which offer many advantages, especially for fast motor-boats.

COOLING SYSTEMS

The most simple, but not nearly the best, method of engine cooling is that whereby the water in which the vessel floats is directly pumped through the engine. This system in any case requires an easily cleaned filter between the cooling water inlet and the pump. This cooling method has the drawback that fine dirt particles in the external water are pumped through the engine, because the filter only retains rather coarse particles. This will cause wear and tear of the cooling-water pump, while parts of the cooling system may become clogged, with resultant overheating and cracking of the engine block. Moreover, in sea water, fouling by salt sediment and more severe corrosion will occur. A closed cooling system in which the cooling water for the engine is kept separate from the external water by means of a heat exchanger does not present these disadvantages, so that closed systems are increasingly being applied. For small engines in steel craft it is usually sufficient to lead the cooling water through a tank the outer wall of which is formed by part of the ship's hull below the water-line. With wooden craft a looped pipe through which the cooling water is pumped can be fitted to the outside of the hull below the water-line. For this purpose several manufacturers of engines supply special coolers which are fixed to the outside of the hull. (Fig. 13.) For large engines use is made of a heat exchanger which is installed in the engine-room, and two cooling water pumps, one which pumps the external water and one which pumps the engine-cooling water through the cooler. In a closed cooling system a cooling water expansion or header tank must be mounted above the engine, so that the cooling system is always filled with water.

It should be borne in mind that, as in the case of all other openings in the hull below the water-line, the cooling water inlet must be capable of being shut off by means of an easily accessible sea-cock. An efficient thermometer for the cooling water within the helmsman's range of vision is essential. The thermometer should be connected to the cylinder-block.

At present air-cooled engines for ships are coming on to the

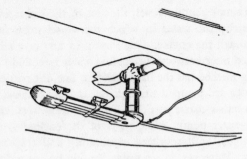

Fig. 13

market. These engines have the disadvantage that they are noisier than the water-cooled ones. With air-cooled engines it is of paramount importance that the engine-room should have an ample air inlet, while the exhaust cooling air has to be carried off directly to the deck, through a duct of sufficient capacity. If this is neglected over-heating of the engine will be the inevitable result. The advantages of an air-cooled engine are a simpler cooling system which is not liable to damage by frost or dirt.

LUBRICATION

For lubrication of the engine and the gearbox the instructions of the manufacturers set out in their instruction manual should be carefully followed. The use of too much or too little oil, or of the wrong quality, may soon lead to serious defects. As the oil-life is limited owing to contamination, oil changes must be regulated by the number of working hours. These can be recorded in an engine log, but nowadays special counters are available, which are not expensive. The engine must be installed in such a way that the oil plugs of the sump, the gearbox and reduction gears, if present, can be reached without acrobatics, and that there also be some room left to place a driptray underneath. One should never allow the old oil to run into the bilge; this would increase the risk of fire. An efficient oil-pressure gauge within the helmsman's range of vision is essential.

The engine should be conveniently arranged so that all parts are easy of access. The engine-room should be kept clean because only then can troubles be rapidly traced and repaired. Keeping a simple engine log-book is highly desirable. In this log-book a note can be made of the parts that have been repaired or renewed, of working hours, fuel consumption, oil consumption, oil change, and defects that have to be checked. A number of unpleasant surprises will be avoided in this way.

The manufacturer supplies a manual with each engine. This manual should be carefully read and its instructions followed. If the engine is second-hand and no longer accompanied by a manual, the manufacturer concerned can always provide one, though not, perhaps, free of charge. The manual gives directions about maintenance, operation and the remedy for defects. As each type of engine has its own peculiarities this book will not go farther into the matter.

IV. Outboard Motors

OUTBOARD MOTORS have the advantage of presenting a complete, portable unit ready for use. This is especially important in winter, because the entire engine, including propeller-shaft and propeller, can be taken home and cleaned, or taken to the repair shop for a check up and maintenance.

Nowadays there are outboard motors on the market ranging in power from $\frac{1}{2}$ to 100 h.p. suitable for propelling all sizes of craft from the smallest open boats to large cabin-cruisers. The majority of these motors work at very high revs. because they are primarily designed for speed. By choosing the right propeller an outboard motor can be adapted to a particular vessel. The heavier motors cannot be very well used as auxiliary motors for sailing yachts because their efficiency for this purpose is too low. The application of outboard motors for use in hydroplanes is unlimited. It should, however, be observed that it is not very wise to fit a boat designed for a 20 or 30 h.p. motor with a motor of 60 or 70 h.p. Apart from the insufficiently robust construction of the hull, its shape is often not suitable for speeds of 40 or 50 miles an hour. In addition it is advisable to consider the fuel consumption of a very powerful motor (0·09–0·11 gallon per h.p. per hour); it may then appear that a somewhat lighter motor is preferable, the more so since a motor that is twice as powerful does not double the speed of the vessel. There is, moreover, another consideration: in many lakes, rivers and canals speed limits are imposed.

The thrust that is delivered by the motor via the transom to the hull is very great with a powerful motor. The reinforcement of the transom and of the adjacent members must be specially designed for the particular motor. In some cases these parts appear to be unequal to their task: the seams around the transom begin to work. In such cases the weak areas must be reinforced as soon as possible. If one waits until the transom comes adrift the cost of repair will be much higher.

It is advisable to add a retaining chain or steel wire by means of which the motor is connected to an eye on the transom, because this may save the motor should it vibrate free or be knocked loose in a collision. To this end many motors are in fact provided with an eye.

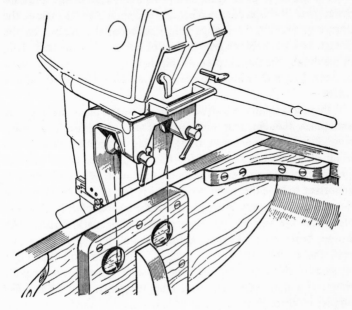

Fig. 14

The security of the motor is considerably improved by counter-sinking recesses about 0·2 in. deep on the inboard face of the transom for the clamp screws. (Fig. 14.) If the motor is left on the boat for the entire season, the bolts should be locked with a chain or a shackle and padlock; this precaution cannot entirely prevent theft, but it will make it much harder.★

★ In Britain insurance of a boat and its equipment does not automatically include cover against the risk of dropping an outboard motor overboard. Insurers will always include this risk on request, sometimes at a slight extra premium.

An outboard motor should never be left on the transom of a dinghy which is being towed at sea. It should be unshipped and *secured* in the dinghy as nearly amidships and as low down as possible. For short trips, although the method imposes some strain on the dinghy, it is reasonable to fix it by its clamps to the middle of the midships thwart; but, if this is done, a piece of wood should be laid first on the thwart to prevent the clamps from damaging the varnish on the thwart. It is advisable to keep a piece of *soft* wood about 10 in. long in the dinghy for this purpose. If this method is used the shaft must be made fast in the dinghy to prevent the engine moving about in a seaway.

Adhere strictly to the instructions given by the manufacturer. It is sometimes thought that outboard motors are difficult to start. Nowadays this is no longer true; starting difficulties are only the result of wrong treatment. If the fuel supply is sufficient and the ignition functions properly, the motor *must* start. When starting, it is important to have the motor turning fairly fast so that the air flow in the carburettor is sufficiently great to make a good mixture, the compression is adequate and the magneto gives a fair spark. Starting with a rope starter should be done as follows: pull the toggle $\frac{3}{4}$–2 inches until the ratchet attachment catches. After that pull the toggle vigorously; this should not be done too slowly, but not too rapidly either. If a motor does not start after ten pulls, shut off the fuel supply, go through the motions of starting a few times to clear the excess fuel and try again. Should the motor still fail to start, then have a look at the sparking-plug, because it will probably have become short-circuited by carbon and fuel. Unless a self-winding toggle is attached to the engine make sure that you have a proper toggle.

MOTOR OVERBOARD!

If, in spite of the retaining chain, the motor should be dropped overboard but soon afterwards recovered, then stick to the following rules:

1. Never try to start the motor until all the water has been drained.
2. Gently pull on the starter toggle to feel whether everything still runs smoothly, after first having removed the sparking-plug(s), then pull the toggle a few times to remove the water from the motor through the sparking-plug sockets. If the water appears to contain mud, stop at once and clean the inside of the motor, or have it cleaned.
3. Pour a little lubricating oil or a mixture of petrol and oil into the sparking-plug sockets and pull the toggle to disperse this lubricant.
4. Clean, dry and replace the sparking-plug(s).
5. Start the motor and, as soon as it runs, squirt a little oil through the air inlet of the carburettor. If the motor fails to start after two or three pulls, then stop and take it to a workshop. Let the motor run for at least two hours to get everything thoroughly dry. Note that the propeller unit must be immersed whilst doing this so that the engine is properly cooled.

A FEW HINTS

Always store cans of petrol upright, cap uppermost.

Never start an outboard motor on which petrol has been spilt until all petrol has evaporated.

Keep a tool-kit on board, containing the tools supplied with the motor, with an additional screwdriver, adjustable spanner and a pair of combination pliers. In addition a spare shear pin for the propeller, a few cotter-pins, a sparking-plug, a torch, a knife, and a tube of gearbox grease or oil as prescribed by the manufacturer; and a feeler gauge to adjust the spark gap. And finally, in a plastic cover, the manual.

Never turn the propeller of an outboard motor unless the motor is in neutral gear or unless the ignition cables have been taken off.

TRAILERS

With the increasing popularity of small, lightweight boats the use of trailers for transporting them has rapidly increased. It should be borne in mind that a trailer has legally to meet the same safety requirements as a car. Hence only use a good, suitably constructed trailer provided with licence plate and lights and with brakes.* In addition the insurance company covering the boat and the car will have to be notified. In Britain the mere fact that your insurance company acknowledges that you use a trailer means only that they will hold you covered for the damage that you do to other people and their property when you are using it. If you want to be insured against loss of or damage to your trailer special arrangements must be made and the value of the trailer declared. It is usually more convenient to *notify* your motor insurance company of the use of the trailer and to insure the trailer itself with the company which insures the boat carried on it.

As for the boat, it must be evenly and properly supported and carefully secured; the outboard motor must be taken off the transom. The motor should either be secured in the boat or carried in the car.

Most trailers are not fit to be driven into the water when launching the boat: the hubs are not waterproof, nor are they resistant to a sudden lowering of temperature.

* In Britain brakes are obligatory in any trailer above two hundredweight in unladen weight.

V. Electrical Installation

As HAS been mentioned in Chapter II, great care should be given to the electrical installation in order to prevent undesirable sparks and defects. A spark may be the cause of an explosion.

BATTERIES

Batteries should be suitably secured in wooden boxes, if possible outside the engine-room. The boxes of lead-acid batteries should be lined with lead and shaped in such a way that the sulphuric acid cannot run into the bilge if a battery-cell is damaged. The batteries should be placed in a well-ventilated space because, during charging, explosive gas is generated. (Fig. 15.) A battery should never be placed under a fuel tank.

The starter motor is the largest consumer of current; hence never run the self-starter for more than fifteen seconds at a time; then allow the battery sufficient time to recover. Two types of batteries are suitable for use in yachts, viz. the lead-acid battery, which is used in nearly all motor-cars, and the alkaline battery, which is used for large installations and for traction purposes.

THE LEAD-ACID BATTERY

If a lead-acid battery is regularly discharged and charged, as in motor-cars, the battery will require little maintenance and have a long service life.

However, in a yacht things are quite different: the charging periods are often insufficient if the engine is operated for only a few hours. Regular inspection, at least once a year, by the manufacturer or his representative is to be recommended. For the maintenance of the battery the following rules should be observed:

Fig. 15

1. The battery should be securely fixed.

2. The battery should be clean and dry, and the terminals should be greased with acid-free vaseline.

3. At least once a month the acid level should be checked and, if necessary, the battery topped up with distilled water, about $\frac{1}{4}$ to $\frac{1}{2}$ in. above the plates, according to the manufacturer's directions.

4. The acid content of the cells should be checked monthly; the specific gravity should be at least 1·24.

5. In winter the batteries should be removed and properly stored.

THE ALKALINE BATTERY

The alkaline battery is more expensive than the lead-acid battery, but its service life is proportionately longer.

The alkaline battery offers considerable advantages for use in a yacht. The battery can stand up to improper treatment, such as over-charging or over-loading, and requires little maintenance. In winter the battery can be left partly discharged, without ill effects; only the fluid level should be watched and if necessary topped up with distilled water. If an alkaline battery is used as a starter battery, a type with a very low internal resistance should be used. The types with normal internal resistance are not capable of supplying, for a short period, the very strong current required by the starter motor. The lead-acid battery delivers 2 volts per cell, the alkaline battery 1·2 volts.

ELECTRIC WIRING

The batteries should be installed as near as possible to the starter motor so as to keep the resistance in the cables as low as possible. For the wiring between battery and starter motor special battery cables of adequate thickness should be used. The starter relay should be mounted on top of or close to the starter motor. All cables, including those for electric lighting, should be properly fixed to wooden or metal cable-ways with saddles at a maximum interval of 12 inches, so that vibration and chafing of the insulation will not be possible. The cable-ways should be installed as high as possible, never under the cabin sole. The wiring must be provided with fuses in special, commercially available fuse-boxes. It is a great advantage to have the installation fitted with a switchboard on which are mounted a main switch, and a switch and fuse for each group. (Fig. 16.) This switchboard should never be installed in the engine-room, in view of possible sparks from the switches, and it should, moreover, be placed as far from the compass as possible. Care should be taken that the electric wiring is not laid near exhaust pipes or other sources of heat, and that it is protected in those places where loose objects may cause damage.

The cross-sections of the cables used in the system must be in accordance with the following table (I)

TABLE I

CROSS-SECTION OF CABLES FOR DIFFERENT AMPERAGES

Nominal Cross-section		Current Rating for Rubber or P.V.C. in Amps
sq. in.	sq. mm.	
·0015	*1·0*	7
·002		9
·003	*1·5*	11
	2·5	14
·0045		16
	4·0	19
·007		21
·01	*6·0*	25
·0145		31
	10·0	34
·0225	*16·0*	44

N.B. Cables with a mineral or Butyl rubber insulation have a higher current rating. The insulation
of the cables must be waterproof.

GENERATORS AND MOTORS

The generators and the starter motor, if placed in the engine-room or mounted on the engine, should be spark proof, which means that they should be totally enclosed or provided with fine-mesh copper gauze in all ventilation openings. (Fig. 17.) The switches in the en-gine-room should also be spark proof.

The electrical installation can be made in several voltages: in small yachts 6- or 12-volt installations adjusted to the voltage of the starter

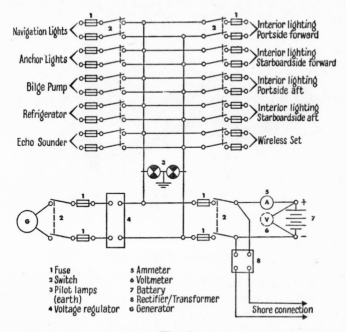

Navigation Lights

Anchor Lights

Bilge Pump

Refrigerator

Echo Sounder

Interior lighting
Portside forward

Interior lighting
Starboardside forward

Interior lighting
Portside aft

Interior lighting
Starboardside aft

Wireless Set

1 Fuse
2 Switch
3 Pilot lamps
  (earth)
4 Voltage regulator

5 Ammeter
6 Voltmeter
7 Battery
8 Rectifier/Transformer
9 Generator

Shore connection

Fig. 16

Note that the electrical installation must be of the flow and return type with two fully insulated conductors to avoid galvanic action and electro-chemical decay.

motor and the generator of the particular engine should be used. For larger vessels this voltage may be increased to 24, 32, or even 110. The advantage of a higher voltage is that wire of smaller diameter will suffice; the loss of energy is also smaller with high voltages than it is with low voltages. With larger yachts it is advisable to install a separate generator, driven by a petrol or diesel engine, with its own batteries. This has the advantage that one can install, independently of the engine, a system with a higher voltage and that does not risk running down the starter batteries when the engine is not in use. The reliability of the system is thereby increased.

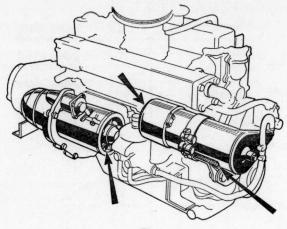

Fig. 17

DESIGN OF THE INSTALLATION

The manufacturer indicates the capacity of a battery in ampere-hours (*Ah*) at 10 or 20 hours' discharge. This means that a battery of 110/120 *Ah* can supply a current of 110/10 = 11 amps. for 10 hours, and a current 120/20 = 6 amps. for 20 hours. If a battery is discharged rapidly, the capacity is lower than when the discharge takes place gradually. If the discharge period is longer than 20 hours, the highest value is the criterion. Hence the above battery supplies, for instance, for 60 hours, a current of 120/60 = 2 amps. or for 100 hours a current of 120/100 = 1·2 amps.

The power carried by an electric wire is expressed in watts (watt = volt × ampere). Accordingly a current of 10 amps. in a 6-volt system has the same power as a current of 5 amps. at 12 volts and 2½ amps. at 24 volts. As the diameter of the wiring is determined by the amperage only, it is clear that at a stronger current a thinner wire can be used for the same power.

With increasing voltage the loss of energy will decrease. Hence the voltage for a particular yacht should be as high as possible: for yachts up to 40 or 45 feet 12 volts, above that 24 or 32 volts.

The capacity of the battery should be sufficient to feed the electrical system for at least 20 hours. In order to determine this capacity an estimate of the consumption of current should be made, for instance as follows:

Interior lighting, 3 lamps of 25 watts each; exterior, 4 navigation lights of 40 watts each. In this case it will be assumed that every 20 hours each lamp will be switched on for 3 hours.

Lighting

$3 \times 25 + 4 \times 40$ =235 watts $\times$ 3 hours = 700 watt/hours.

Wireless set   80 watts $\times$ 5 hours = 400 watt/hours.

Echo sounder   30 watts $\times$ 4 hours = 120 watt/hours.

Total 1220 watt/hours.

1220 watt hours/12 volt = 102 ampere/hours.

Hence a battery of 100 Ah at 12 volts would be sufficient for the above system.

In addition it should be established what appliances will be used simultaneously. The total amperage of these appliances must be calculated. In the above example this could be as follows:

1 lamp	at 25 watt 12 volt 2A (watt = volt $\times$ amp.)	
4 lamps	at 40 watt 12 volt 13$\frac{1}{2}$ A	
Wireless	at 80 watt 12 volt 6$\frac{1}{2}$ A	
Echo sounder	at 30 watt 12 volt 2$\frac{1}{2}$ A	
	24$\frac{1}{2}$ A	

The capacity of the battery must be adequate to supply 24$\frac{1}{2}$ amps. for a discharging period of 10 hours, which means that the battery of 100 Ah is too light for this installation. The battery must have a capacity of 245 Ah at a discharging period of 10 hours.

If separate batteries are used for starting and lighting, the engine should preferably have two generators, one for the starter battery and one for the lighting battery. These generators should be specially made for sea-going use, and should be completely enclosed or made spark free by means of fine-mesh wire gauze. The capacity in amps.

of the generator should be approximately fifty per cent higher than the capacity per hour of the battery at a discharging period of 10 hours. Hence a battery of 110/120 *Ah* requires a generator of 110/10 × 1·5 = 16·5 ampere capacity. The generator must be provided with a voltage regulator; this regulator keeps the voltage constant at different revolutions, cuts the connection with the battery when the engine stops, and prevents the battery from being overcharged.

It is advisable to install the system in such a way that the various appliances are mutually earthed by means of a cable which is either connected to the hull in one place only or not connected to the hull at all. For the positive as well as for the negative line a cable must be used, so that the current is not discharged through the hull, as it is in the case of motor-cars.

If the boat is often occupied when lying at a permanent berth, it is a good idea to install a transformer on board in order to maintain

TABLE II

SUITABLE WIRING FOR MINIMUM LOSS OF VOLTAGE

Nominal Cross-section		Loss of Voltage in Volts per Amp	
sq. in.	sq. mm.	per Foot of Cable	per Metre of Cable
·0015		·0067	
	1·0		·0175
·002		·0049	
	1·5		·0117
·003		·0031	
	2·5		·0070
·0045		·0019	
	4·0		·0044
·007		·0012	
	6·0		·0029
·0145		·0008	
	10·0		·0018
·0225		·0005	
	16·0		·0011

the charge in the batteries by means of current from ashore. For interior lighting it can be assumed that 10 watt per 10 sq. ft. of horizontal surface is sufficient for the accommodation concerned, in small cabins possibly a little more.

If all appliances are to function properly the loss of voltage in the wiring should not exceed a certain amount. The loss of voltage depends on the total length of the circuit. In the lighting wiring and between lamp and switchboard the maximum loss may be 3 per cent, which means 0·18 v at 6 v, 0·36 v at 12 v, and 0·72 v at 24 v. In the wire leads between the source of the current and the switchboard a loss of voltage of 2 per cent is permissible, which means 0·12 v, 0·24 v and 0·48 v, respectively. With the aid of the table (II) on page 46 it can be determined whether the wiring meets these requirements.

VI. Ventilation

IN ORDER to keep the atmosphere on board fresh and to prevent the development of rot in wooden and of rust in steel vessels good ventilation is essential. Many yachts have inadequate facilities for proper ventilation.

Under normal conditions a boat when sailing, and also when at anchor, is ventilated from stern to bow. If an attempt is made to alter this, the ventilation will not be very effective and the air in the ship may become stagnant. The principle of ventilation from stern to bow should be followed as far as possible, and the space below the cabin sole must be included in this plan. (Fig. 18.)

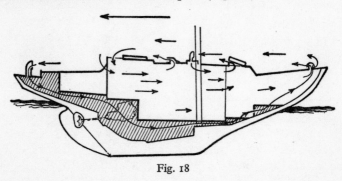

Fig. 18

To ensure good ventilation air must be able to circulate freely between the panelling and the hull and also between linings and deckheads athwartships and from bilge to deckhead between the frames. There should therefore always be a clearance between the cabin sole and the hull: this also holds good for shelves and lockers. All locker doors should be provided with ventilation openings at the top and at the bottom. (Fig. 19.) A ship with insufficient ventilation can be recognized immediately by its musty smell. Once the ventilation is effective, the air on board is fresh.

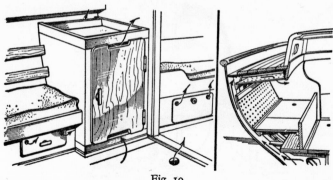

Fig. 19

Good ventilation is especially important during bad weather; during good weather a sufficient amount of fresh air will enter through open doors, scuttles and hatches. During bad weather the ventilators and specially designed hatches are the only sources of fresh air.

The six most important types of ventilators for use on board yachts are:

1. *The mushroom ventilator.* The top of this ventilator, which screws down into position, must be able to close properly. This type of ventilator is only suitable for the extraction of air as are the cowls which are often fitted to the sides of the cabins in motor yachts. (Fig. 20.)

2. *The ordinary cowl*, possibly placed on a water trap. This combination is called the *Dorade* ventilator, after the yacht on which this

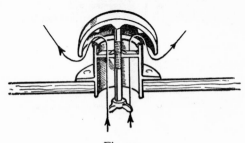

Fig. 20

D

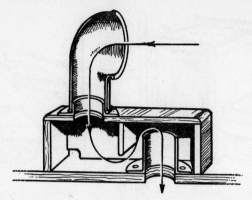

Fig. 21

system was used for the first time by the Stephens brothers. This *Dorade* is very efficient, especially for air intake, although a small amount of air is wasted through the scupper holes. (Fig. 21.)

3. *The venturi ventilator*, which has to be turned to the wind to function properly. (Fig. 22.)

4. *The ventilating box with built-in water trap*. This type is satisfactory for forced ventilation, as long as no great quantities of spray drive against the air inlet. (Fig. 23.)

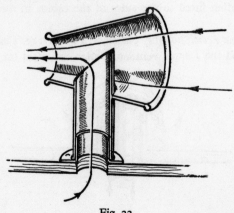

Fig. 22

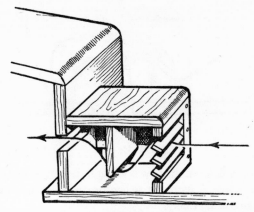

Fig. 23

5. *The cowling with built-in water trap.* This type is very good but very expensive. (Fig. 24.)
6. *The cowl for air intake and extraction.* This type is only suitable for forced ventilation. (Fig. 25.)

Apart from the above types there are several other makes, which all have their merits and drawbacks. However, the most important types are set out above.

Fig. 24

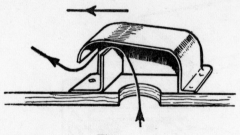

Fig. 25

A built-in ventilator in the bow is all right, as long as one does not sail in rough waters. A ventilator so constructed cannot, however, be cleaned or painted internally.

There should preferably be a gas-tight bulkhead between the engine-room and the other parts of the ship; the lower part of the bulkhead should in addition be oil-proof. With a diesel engine gas-tightness is not strictly necessary as long as the engine is in good condition and no leakage of diesel oil occurs. As in the long run most diesel installations will develop some leaks, only a good oil-proof and gas-tight separation of the engine-room will fully guarantee the absence of engine smells in the ship. The engine-room should have at least two ventilating ducts opening on to the deck. In case of a petrol engine there should be a spark-proof electric extraction fan on one of these ducts. As soon as the engine runs, the air consumption of the engine will ensure a sufficient change of air; before starting, however, the engine-room of a petrol engine should be well venti-lated. An air-cooled engine should in addition have a duct for used cooling air taken up to deck level. If a duct is not fitted the cooling air will circulate in the engine-room and as a result become too hot for cooling the engine. (Fig. 26.)

A skylight in the coach roof or in the deck makes a good ventilator, but when it is poorly constructed it can be a constant nuisance, because leaks can easily occur. Moreover, the old-fashioned type of construction has the disadvantage that cordage gets caught under the overlap of the closed cover. A design developed in England for sea-

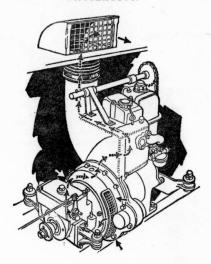

Fig. 26

going yachts is shown in Fig. 27. For the fo'c'sle hatch and the cabin hatch the same considerations apply. A modern development is a fore-hatch which can be hinged fore or aft at will, and which is provided with retractable flaps at each side to prevent rain driving in from the side. (Fig. 28.) In sailing yachts the construction of the fore-hatch should be very strong, because the crew when working on the foredeck will stand on and brace themselves against it. The sliding-hatch on the cabin should slide easily, since this entrance is used most. A hatch which is stiff to slide will be a constant source of irritation. Easy sliding can only be achieved by careful construction with runners that are both horizontally and vertically fitted with metal strips. (Fig. 29.) It is as well to remember in the case of all openings on deck that water must be disposed of not only in calm weather but also in a high wind, without being blown inside. Frequently this will not be a simple matter, but with forethought and experience a good solution can always be found.

Natural ventilation will not, under all conditions, be capable of effecting a sufficient air change above the cooker. An electric fan will

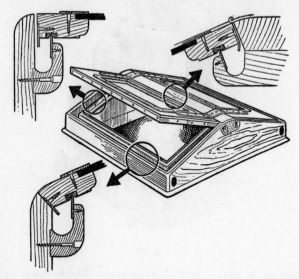

Fig. 27

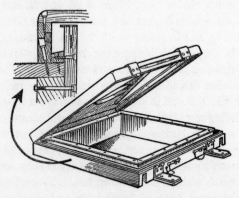

Fig. 28

The diagrams on this page are reproduced by courtesy of Mr Bernard Hayman and *Yachting World*.

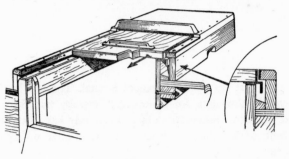

Fig. 29

come in very useful, but it has one disadvantage: the blades of the fan and the extractor vent will become fouled by grease deposits. Hence a model should be chosen that can be easily cleaned.

In spring and autumn it can be very pleasant to have a coal fire in the cabin. In Britain special stoves are made for this purpose, which occupy little space and draw very well. Such a stove should preferably be placed forward in the cabin, because in that way the natural ventilation from stern to bow is intensified. A few holes in the sole in front of the stove or an air duct should keep the air under the sole in constant movement. In the western European climate in summer this type of stove will also come in very handy; it keeps both ship and clothes dry.

Wet sea boots also belong to this chapter! As is well known, it takes a few days before they get thoroughly dry, unless a piece of cardboard is placed in the leg of each boot, so that a downward and an upward air stream can develop. The drying time is then halved.

VII. Equipment

FOR SAFETY at sea good equipment is vital. The law lays down extensive requirements for commercial vessels, but for private pleasure craft this important subject is entirely left to the owner. As a result unnecessary accidents occur fairly often owing to imperfect equipment.

MOORING ROPES

For mooring open boats rope is all too often employed which can no longer be used for halyards or sheets. The owners are under the impression that such rope is still good enough to use as a painter. Nothing is farther from the truth; in a strong wind or a gale painters, and also the bollards and cleats on which they are made up, will have a rough time. Often, especially with small yachts, the cleats are too small for a fair-sized painter to be properly belayed. The fixing of the cleat to the deck appears in many cases to be quite insufficient, and a reinforcement under the deck is frequently lacking. Hard-and-fast rules for dimensions and reinforcements for bollards and cleats are difficult to give. For a given thickness of line a cleat or bollard should be selected to which that line can be properly secured. The cleat or bollard must be bolted to the deck. The deck must be rein-

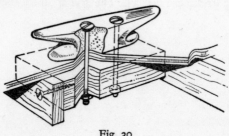

Fig. 30

forced underneath with a hardwood backing piece running at least from deck-beam to deck-beam and secured to both deck-beams. (Fig. 30.) Table III gives the proper size of mooring ropes for larger craft.

TABLE III

SIZE OF MOORING ROPE RELATED TO SIZE OF CRAFT

Overall Length		Nylon		Manila	
Feet	Metres	Circumf. in.	Diameter mm.	Circumf. in.	Diameter mm.
to 20	to 6	1–1¼	10	1¼–1¾	14–16
20–26	6–8	1½	12	1¾–2¼	16–18
26–40	8–12	1½	12	2¼–2½	18–20
40–50	12–15	1¾–2	14–16	2½–2¾	20–22

For the qualities of various types of rope, refer to Chapter XIV.

NAVIGATION LIGHTS

Every vessel under way or at anchor between sunset and sunrise is required to carry the lights prescribed in the *International Regulations for Preventing Collisions at Sea* (1948).* Good lights are as important on the water as on the road, especially on crowded waterways, such as the Rhine and Waal in Holland or the Thames Estuary and Solent in England, and in large ports.

Small oil lamps have the drawback that they do not give sufficient light and that they are easily blown out. Hence electric lights are preferable. The lights of pleasure craft are often not strong enough; 6-watt bulbs are definitely inadequate. The illumination of yachts is shown in Fig. 31.

Lights should be clearly visible under all conditions. In sailing yachts particularly it frequently happens that a sail entirely masks one of the side-lights. This of course is quite illegal. Yachts making a passage during the hours of darkness at sea or in major waterways are

* See page 108 *et seq.*

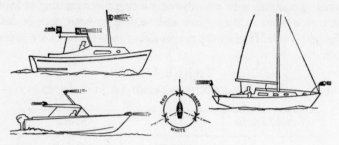

Fig. 31

well advised to have an Aldis signalling lamp or white flares at hand with which to warn sea-going vessels of their presence. From a lofty bridge the lights of a yacht, low on the water, are very difficult to see, especially when the vessels are fairly close to each other. (See the *International Regulations*.)

RADAR REFLECTOR

For yachts at sea at night or in fog a radar reflector is also nowadays a most desirable piece of equipment.

SIREN OR WHISTLE

Every steam or motor-vessel must have a siren with which clear sound signals can be given. In motor-yachts this is often a fixed horn operated by compressed air or electricity. Sailing yachts under sail should make sound signals with a fog-horn at sea. The helmsman should be able to use the horn without leaving the tiller or the wheel. Motor-yachts that sail the large rivers on the Continent are advised to carry a yellow signal lantern. This lantern gives a clear all-round yellow light and is connected in parallel to the siren. (Fig. 32.) On other waterways, too, the signal lantern may be very useful. Yachtsmen on the Dutch, Belgian and French rivers *must* learn the local signalling rules, which are not very difficult, and the rules of the road which are different for various waterways. Special rules also apply

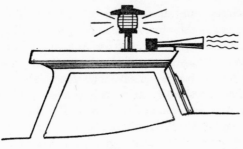

Fig. 32

to the waters under the control of the Port of London Authority. In case of doubt as to whether there are special regulations in any English waterways or harbours the relevant Admiralty Pilot should be consulted; for inland waterways the regulations laid down by the local authority can usually be easily obtained.

FOG-HORN AND BELL

To be able to give the fog-signals prescribed by law every powered vessel must be provided with a fog-horn, for which the siren may be used. In addition, a ship's bell must be carried on board all yachts, should the craft lie at anchor in a fog.

COMPASS

A compass is vital if one is going to sail in the open sea and it is really an essential piece of equipment for coastal cruising. When installing the compass it should be realized that all iron or steel objects in its vicinity may cause deviation. The ideal place for a compass is amidships, at least 1 ft. from any electric wiring, 3 ft. from electric apparatus, including wireless sets, and 6 ft., if possible, from any substantial iron component. In steel-built yachts this last requirement can hardly ever be met. This is not, however, an insuperable difficulty, because the deviation caused by the presence of metal can be reduced to reasonable proportions by adjusting the compass. Two other requirements must, however, be satisfied. Special care should be taken that no movable objects of iron or steel, such as a gear lever for instance, are placed near the compass. Any such necessary objects should be made of brass, bronze or aluminium. A table in the neigh-bourhood of the compass is not advisable: iron objects, for instance a pair of pliers or a shackle, accidentally placed on this table may cause a dangerous deviation of the compass. The electric wiring for the compass lighting should consist of two twisted cores that will not induce a magnetic field. To be sure of one's compass it is advisable to have it checked and adjusted by a qualified compass adjuster. Even after this has been done the compass should be checked on every possible occasion by bearings on fixed objects.

WIRELESS

Sensible safety precautions include the use of radio weather fore-casts. It does occasionally happen that weather forecasts do not come off, but this is an exception and is no reason to ignore them. A good skipper makes his plans in accordance with the weather forecasts.

The English weather forecast for shipping is broadcast on the BBC Light Programme on 1500 m. (200 kc/s), on Sundays at 06.45 hours, 11.55 hours and 17.58 hours G.M.T. On week-days at 06.45 hours; 13.40 hours, 17.58 hours and 00.02 hours G.M.T. The English gale warnings are broadcast in the Light Programme at the end of the programme. For these weather forecasts the British Meteorological Office uses the areas shown in Fig. 33. Every yachts-man should learn by heart the Beaufort Scale of wind force as all weather forecasts use this notation.

BILGE PUMP

Every yacht should be provided with an efficient and easily operated bilge pump with suction pipes installed in such a way that water from each part of the ship can be pumped overboard. Valves and cocks should be readily accessible and the outlet through the

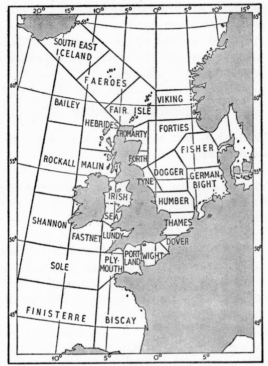

Fig. 33

TABLE IV

CAPACITY AND SIZE OF SUCTION PIPE RELATED TO SIZE OF CRAFT

Overall Length		Capacity	Int. Diameter	
Feet	Metres	tons/hour	ins.	mm.
to 20	*to 6*	$1\frac{1}{2}$	$\frac{3}{4}$	20
20–26	*6–8*	2	1	25
26–40	*8–12*	3	$1\frac{1}{4}$	35
40–50	*12–15*	4	$1\frac{1}{2}$	40

vessel's side should be fitted with a sea-cock directly on the hull. Table IV serves as a guide for capacity and size of the suction pipe.

The diameter of the piston of the suction pump should be twice the diameter of the suction pipe. The ends of the bilge lines must be provided with strum boxes (strainers).

LIGHTNING CONDUCTOR

Although it hardly ever happens that a yacht is damaged by lightning, it is a wise precaution to install a reliable lightning conductor; one must remember that lightning will always take the shortest way, via metal, to the water. If a wooden mast projects above the rigging, the wood above the rigging will be split if struck by lightning. At the lower end of the rigging the lightning finds its way to the water via the chain plates. If the chain plates are fixed to the inside of the hull, the lightning will make a hole in the hull through which it finds its way from the chain plates to the water. This can be prevented by connecting the chain plates to the keelbolts by means of copper strips. In that case the keelbolts should be well home to the metal keel so as not to cause resistance. A connection between the forestay and the ironwork on the ship's stem might also produce the desired result, but since the route via the shrouds is shorter, it is always possible that the lightning will miss the forestay.

To protect the truck, a copper strip should be fitted from the top of the shrouds to the truck. Lloyd's Register of Shipping recommend in their *Rules for Yachts* that the lightning conductor should be made of copper strip or cable having a cross section of $0 \cdot 15$ in.^{2}, connected to a copper point with a diameter of $\frac{1}{2}$ in., which should project at least 6 in. above the top of the mast. In a steel-built vessel rigging and hull will act as a perfect conductor without any special installation. The lightning conductor must be as straight as possible and sharp bends should be avoided.

If it is not possible to make an effective earth through the keel, the lightning conductor can be connected to a copper plate attached to the outside of the hull. (Fig. 34.)

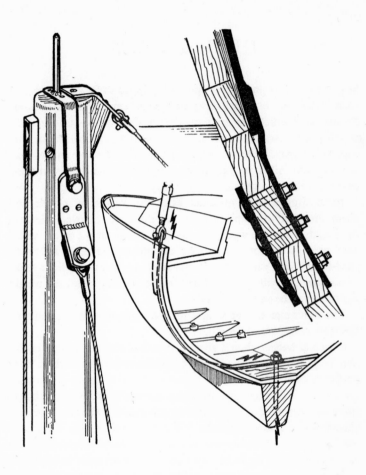

Fig. 34

VIII. Ground Tackle

MANY SMALL yachts are very poorly equipped so far as anchors and anchor cables or chains are concerned. This is mainly due to the conditions under which they are normally sailed: anchoring is frequently unnecessary in waters where a vacant mooring can be found. Circumstances may, however, arise in which a good heavy anchor may save the ship. All larger yachts are equipped with anchors, but these anchors are not always sufficiently heavy.

Table V gives some guidance as to the weight of anchor and chain. In order to simplify the use of the table the overall length, the length along the water-line and the displacement of the vessel have been given; these measurements must be taken to refer to a steel-built sailing yacht with normal overhang. For a very light vessel a lesser weight will suffice, while for a very heavy vessel the weight indicated will be on the light side.

The minimum anchor weight for a motor-yacht can be found on the basis of the overall length.

A second anchor should always be carried and the weight of this may be 75 per cent of the weight of the above anchors, and if a third anchor is carried that may be 50 per cent of the weight of the main anchor. CQR (Plough) and Danforth anchors may be lighter, but to make allowance for different holding grounds ¾ of the above weights should be taken as a minimum. When buying an anchor one should remember that the minimum weight for a suitable anchor is 25 lb. Below this weight an anchor may certainly be serviceable but it will fail to enter hard sandy ground. The same holds true for a stockless anchor of less than 75 lb.

The old-fashioned Admiralty pattern anchor, with or without a folding stock, is still the best anchor for general use. (Fig. 35.) The drawback of these anchors is that they take up a lot of space when stowed on deck or in the fo'c'sle. Moreover, an anchor with a stock

TABLE V

A. WEIGHT OF STOCKED ANCHOR RELATED TO SIZE OF CRAFT

Waterline Length		Overall Length		Displacement	Weight of Stocked Anchor	
Feet	Metres	Feet	Metres	Tons	Lb.	Kg.
20	6	30	9	4	45	20
23	7	33	10	5·5	55	25
26	8	36	11	8	65	30
30	9	40	12	11	75	35
33	10	45	13·5	14·5	90	40
38	11·5	50	15·5	20·5	100	45
43	13	55	17·5	28	130	60
48	14·5	60	19	37	165	75
55	16·5	70	22	55	210	95

B. SIZE OF ANCHOR CABLE RELATED TO SIZE OF CRAFT

Waterline Length		Anchor Cable			
		Diameter in.	Length		15-fathom lengths
Feet	Metres		Fathoms	Metres	
20	6	$\frac{3}{16}$	30	50	2
23	7	$\frac{1}{4}$	30	50	2
26	8	$\frac{5}{16}$	30	50	2
30	9	$\frac{5}{16}$	35	60	3
33	10	$\frac{3}{8}$	35	60	3
38	11·5	$\frac{3}{8}$	55	100	3
43	13	$\frac{7}{16}$	65	120	4
48	14·5	$\frac{7}{16}$	85	150	4
55	16·5	$\frac{1}{2}$	85	150	4

has the disadvantage that one fluke always projects above the sea bed, so that in a shifting wind or turning tide the anchor cable is liable to

E

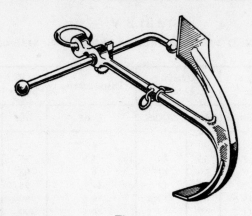

Fig. 35

foul the projecting fluke, and in this way trip the anchor. (Fig. 36.)
When anchoring one should also be careful not to pay out too much
chain at once. If the chain drops on top of the anchor, there is a good
chance that the latter will become fouled. Plough and stockless
anchors do not have this drawback.

An anchor with a stock can be used with a rope cable; but in that
case, the cable should not be too short and one must be certain that

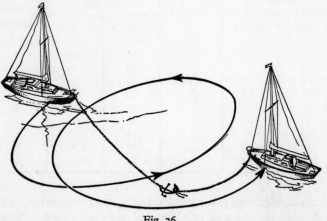

Fig. 36

Fig. 37

the bottom is free from stones or wreckage which could cut the rope. In case of doubt a chain cable should be used. An added advantage of chain over rope is that through its own weight it also acts as an anchor and shock-absorber.

If the chain is hauled in by means of a winch, a swivelling link should be inserted between anchor and chain, because otherwise difficulties may arise on weighing anchor. (Fig. 37.)

The plough CQR anchor consists of a shank to which a double-sided ploughshare with a weighted point is hinged. (Fig. 38.) This

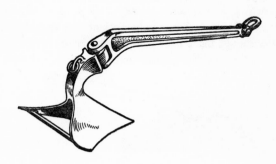

Fig. 38

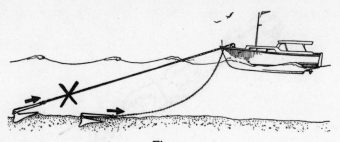

Fig. 39

anchor will always fall in such a way that it digs itself in. In addition, it is not necessary to be particularly careful when paying out the chain. It is even a good idea to pay out a fair length at once, so that the anchor is pulled hard into the ground with the chain almost horizontal. This anchor can never be used without a chain, nor indeed without a length of chain, because without the weight of a chain the shank is pulled obliquely upwards with the result that the anchor will be broken out. (Fig. 39.)

The stockless anchor is increasingly used for sea-going and inland commercial craft, because it is easy to stow and will hardly ever foul. It is usually carried with the shank in the hawse-pipe and the flukes on the outside against the hull. It consists of a heavy, straight shank with a pin at the end, around which the two flukes can rotate in both directions to about a 25-degree angle. Danforth anchors are made according to the same principle. (Fig. 40.) As mentioned before, the stockless anchor is only efficient if it weighs more than 75 lb. One should make sure that the flukes of the anchor hinge easily, because a stockless anchor which has seized up with rust is

Fig. 40

utterly useless when it reaches the bottom with the flukes pointing upwards.

As a rule small yachts will be sufficiently equipped if the anchor cable is of good rope provided that the first five fathoms of the cable are of chain. On the fo'c'sle a stout bollard or bitts should be mounted for securing the anchor cable. Nowadays nylon is more and more used as an anchor cable, because it is light, strong and highly elastic and absorbs hardly any water. Any vessel more than 33 ft. long, which will require an anchor of more than 90 lb. in weigh, tre-quires an anchor cable of chain only for the main anchor, and a suitable windlass.

When anchoring one rule should always be kept in mind: trust your own anchor better than someone else's, but never trust an anchor completely. The boat's position should be checked regularly by means of a bearing.

In tidal waters it is necessary to veer and shorten cable with the rise and fall of the tide. It is a reasonable rule in most holding grounds to ride to a cable of a length equal to at least three times the depth of the water.

IX. Life-Saving Appliances

LIFE-JACKETS, LIFEBUOYS AND SAFETY-HARNESS

EVERY VESSEL should have at least one life-jacket for everyone on board. In practice this sound rule is often neglected by pleasure craft on inland waterways, although fortunately the situation appears to be improving: in some sailing races the wearing of a life-jacket is compulsory, while many racing helmsmen take this precaution voluntarily.

In former days kapok and cork were used for life-jackets and lifebuoys. Life-jackets filled with kapok have the drawback that they slowly absorb water and rapidly absorb oil, while cork for life-jackets is uncomfortably hard and rather heavy. Nowdays kapok and cork have been replaced by the much lighter and hence more buoyant plastic foam. On board pleasure craft, inflatable life-jackets offer many advantages: they can be stored in a very limited space and can be worn without much inconvenience when work has to be done on deck.

In small craft which are only used for day sailing, it is advisable to have cockpit cushions that can be used as floats, and to have a few life-jackets in an easily accessible place. In vessels bound for the open sea there should be a life-jacket for each member of the crew as well as one or more buoys on deck, ready for use. Lifebuoys should not be too hard or too heavy, but not too light either: a light buoy can be carried off too far by the wind and will drift away too rapidly. Finding one of the crew who has fallen overboard is considerably facilitated if the lifebuoy is provided with a suitable light or similar apparatus.

The best colour for lifebuoys and life-jackets is orange, followed by red and white used in combination. White alone is difficult to see in rough water and red is almost invisible after dark. At present fluorescent colours are being increasingly used. These fluorescent colours are easily visible especially when the light is poor. Tests have shown that visibility of such colours is five times better than that of ordinary colours.

Enormous progress has been made in the field of inflatable life-jackets in the last few years. The simplest jacket is inflated by the mouth; the most elaborate are equipped with lights and inflate automatically. Inflatable jackets must be inspected in the manner specified by the manufacturer, since leakages may occur and the rubber cloth may eventually become porous.

In the last few years coats and waistcoats have been made with an inflatable lining or a lining made of kapok or foam plastic. These articles of clothing have sufficient buoyancy to keep a person afloat but they are both expensive and hot, which may sometimes be an objection.

Clothing in loud colours, such as orange or yellow for oilskins, and especially an orange or yellow cap, may sometimes spell safety for a drowning person. Such colours may also be useful for the yacht itself.

All crew members on deck should wear safety-harness in bad weather and at night. Children should wear harness of the right size under all circumstances when on deck. A safety-harness is useless unless hooked on to the life-lines or some other part of the standing rigging.

DINGHIES AND LIFE-RAFTS

A wooden, aluminium or polyester dinghy on deck or towed behind the vessel is handy and useful in quiet waters and is pleasant for teaching children how to handle a boat. As a life-boat in the open sea such boats are nearly always useless because of their small size. The only good life-boat for pleasure craft is an inflatable raft provided with a cover. Nowadays these inflatable rafts and boats are made in all sizes and qualities, both for merchant vessels and for pleasure craft. Experience has already proved that the chances of survival in an inflatable raft with a cover under all weather conditions are much greater than in an open life-boat, however large and seaworthy this boat may be. For yachts a rubber raft as life-raft is ideal. The rubber rafts are delivered in a bag or container; they are light and occupy little space. A raft with a diameter of 6 ft. which can accommodate four persons and is equipped with a cover, automatic inflation, manual pump, bailer, distress signals, sea anchor, stabilizers and mending outfit, packed in a bag (measuring 2 ft. × 1 ft. × 1 ft., weight 45 lb.), costs about £100 – at the moment. However, cheaper versions are also available.

The inflatable dinghy has the same advantages: it is light and consequently easy to handle, does not damage varnished topsides, has good buoyancy and is highly suitable as a life-boat, provided that it is equipped with a cover. The drawback of rubber rafts and boats is that they need to be checked regularly by the manufacturers because their serviceable life is not unlimited.

FLARES AND ROCKETS

Red flares and rockets as distress signals should be on hand in all yachts that sail in open waters. The most simple flare is the life-boat flare, which is held in the hand. As this flare can never be shown at a great height, its visibility over the horizon is limited. An observer with an eye level of 10 ft. above the level of the sea can see a life-boat flare at the same height up to a distance of, at most, $7\frac{1}{2}$ miles. If the height of the flare is raised from 10 to 20 ft., it will be visible up to a distance of $8\frac{3}{4}$ miles. Hence from the bridge of a steamship the flare of a life-boat or a yacht is also visible at this, and sometimes at even a greater distance. White flares are to be recommended for night use in crowded waters, because under certain circumstances a small vessel is invisible from the bridge of a sea-going ship, even though she carries the prescribed lights.

To draw the attention of ships at a great distance a parachute flare is necessary. This flare is available in the form of a rocket or a cartridge which is fired by a special pistol. With low clouds, however, it may happen that the flare will get above the clouds. For distress signals during the day orange smoke signals are used; however, in a strong wind these are useless because the smoke will be blown away. Generally speaking a flare is at least equally visible during the day.

It can be concluded, to sum up, that life-jackets are desirable in all waters. Sea-going craft must carry life-jackets for the entire crew, and in sailing yachts at sea these life-jackets should always be worn on deck. In addition small yachts at sea and on large inland waterways need life-boat flares – white to avoid being run down, and red as a distress signal. For larger yachts these requirements can be supplemented with a pistol for flares or rockets and with a hand signal-lamp.

MAN OVERBOARD!

If someone falls overboard, the first impulse is usually to turn back as quickly as possible. This is, however, a mistake because rapid turning never takes the boat to the man in the water. First of all a good lifebuoy with a Home's light should be thrown as close to the man as possible, but carefully so that it does not actually hit him. If the crew is sufficiently large, one man should endeavour to keep the man overboard continually in view; in a seaway this is of paramount importance. Before altering course care should be taken to decide on the correct manœuvre. This manœuvre should be carried out in such a way that the ship comes up to the wind, near, and preferably slightly to windward of, the man in the water. In vessels with considerable freeboard it is nearly impossible to lift a fully grown man in waterlogged clothes out of the water and up the boat's side: in those circumstances a normal man can weigh anything up to twenty stone. A portable companion-way, a rope ladder or a rope with a bowline in it are indispensable for this purpose. If the man is wearing a safety-harness he can be got over the side quite easily by hooking the spinnaker or another halyard on to the ring of the harness. Substantial assistance in getting a man back on board

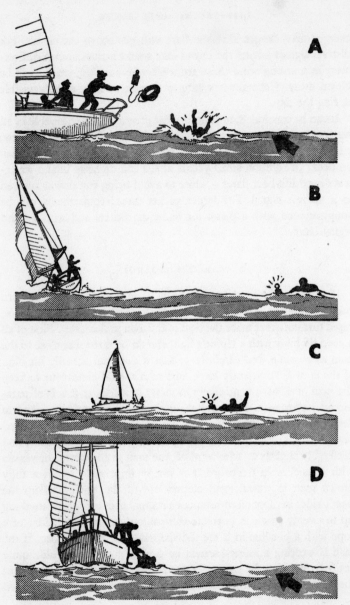

Fig. 41

can be obtained by judicious use of the ship's roll and the movement of the waves. In good weather it is a useful and amusing game to practise 'man overboard'. (Fig. 41.)

THE FIRST-AID BOX

Every yacht should have a complete and well-kept first-aid box. This box should be made of strong, durable and rust-free material. The lid should preferably be watertight. The contents should be conveniently arranged; each bottle or jar should have a label and – if necessary – directions for use.

Any good first-aid handbook will give details of the normal requirements of a first-aid box. Do not, however, forget tablets against seasickness, a thermometer, cream against sunburn and salve for chapped lips; and do not forget that the dressings and drugs should be present in sufficient quantities if an extended voyage is to be undertaken.

The first-aid box must be in a really accessible place and the entire crew should know where to find it. A hot-water bottle is extremely useful in cases of acute chill.

No passage should be begun unless there is on board a well-written first-aid handbook such as the handbooks published by the Red Cross and St John's Ambulance Brigade.

The chapters on artificial respiration and arterial bleeding should be carefully studied in whatever first-aid manual is available and they should be thoroughly practised. A drowning man who has stopped breathing and a casualty with a spouting artery are in such urgent need of help that time lost in feverishly looking up books may be fatal!

X. Laying-up

LAYING-UP is the first step towards the next season. Winter is hardly long enough to do all that has to be done in the way of maintenance, so it is sensible to start overhauling your boat in the autumn. In the autumn, yards usually have time to get things done; in the spring everybody is pressed for time. The owner who forgets this will always be late in getting afloat again.

There are four ways to lay up a boat:

1. Safely stored in a shed.
2. Ashore, under tarpaulins or some other waterproof cover.
3. Afloat, as above.
4. Afloat, and uncovered. This practice is much to be deplored.

The first method is used for practically all open boats. It should be realized that in winter a shed can be very damp, so cordage, sails and other equipment, well cleaned and dried, should be stored at home.

The second method has the disadvantage that repairs and painting can only be done in fair weather. The advantage is that this method is less expensive.

The third method is only employed for large yachts and for boats made of oak, which, in a dry winter, would seriously suffer from drying out and cracking of the planking if they were to be laid up ashore.

The fourth method is only appropriate for boats that are to be broken up.

The manufacturers claim that polyester boats can be left outdoors in winter, provided they are placed upside-down. The author doubts whether this is the best method: polyester does weather, although in a minor degree, so that laying-up in a shed is to be preferred also for this type of boat. In any case it is advisable to check now and then whether everything is still in good order, especially in the autumn after the first heavy rains. The boat must be kept dry inside.

When a boat is laid up, the first thing to do is to clean, dry and stow the sails. Sails that have been used on salt water should be rinsed in fresh water and then dried. The same holds good for ropes. While this is being done a sharp look-out should be kept for defects and damage and any necessary repairs should be carried out.

At the same time as the sails and cordage are removed all the other gear and equipment, including the mattresses, should be taken off and, after thorough cleaning, stored, if necessary with mothballs. When the ship is completely empty, it must be thoroughly cleaned, both internally and externally. The cabin sole should be taken out and all doors should be opened for better ventilation. Engine, lavatory, sink and water-tanks must be drained; while this is being done special attention must be paid to the cocks to see that they are working properly and that no water is left behind; pipes and pumps must also be free from water. Engines which have no closed-circuit cooling system are particularly subject to fouling from the impurities in the cooling water which is drawn from outside the vessel. This may result in clogging of drainage cocks and in water becoming trapped in the cooling system. In that case cylinder-blocks will have a fair chance of freezing. So make sure that all cooling water has been drained off. With engines that have a closed-circuit cooling system it is particularly easy to miss out some operation, so special care must be exercised.

If an engine is due for an overhaul, the best thing to do is to remove it from the vessel, before laying-up. It is much simpler to lift an engine from a floating ship than to do so afterwards in a shed or under a tarpaulin. All pipes leading to the hull below the water-line must be disconnected from the sea-cocks after the latter have been closed.

During these operations it is useful to have paper and pencil at hand, so that all necessary repairs can be noted down at once.

The tarpaulin covering a ship laid up out of doors should be strong to prevent it from being damaged by winter gales. It should fit properly, to prevent it from flapping in the wind, but on the other hand it should not be so tight as to tear the thimbles from the cloth.

There should be a ventilation opening fore and aft, so that fresh air can circulate under the cover. In addition, hatches, scuttles, etc., should be left open, so that fresh air can get in. Gas cylinders should, preferably, be taken out and stored ashore in a well-ventilated room.

Remember that a vessel laid up afloat should be moored with chains or steel wire, because rope will chafe too readily in winter. Ropes can only be used with safety if they are regularly inspected.

When the engine is left on board, a few more steps are to be recommended apart from draining the cooling system, viz.:

1. Let the engine run warm and then drain the cooling water system. In case of petrol engines squirt a little oil into the air inlet of the carburettor just before stopping the engine.

2. Drain the oil from engine, gearbox and, if present, reduction gears, while the engine is still warm, and refill with fresh oil.

3. Remove the sparking-plugs or the injectors from the engine, pour some oil into each cylinder, turn the engine several times and then refit the sparking-plugs or injectors or replace them temporarily with corks.

4. In the case of petrol engines clean the feed pipes and the carburettor and drain the petrol tank (to prevent the formation of gum).

5. Press enough grease in the stern-tube to ensure that all water is removed and no seepage occurs.

6. Disconnect the batteries, remove them from the boat and take them to the manufacturer, his representative, or a battery repair shop for a check-up and winter maintenance. Alkaline batteries, if disconnected, can remain on board.

7. Clean the battery terminals and grease them with acid-free Vaseline.

8. Disconnect the electric equipment of the engine – viz. generator, starter motor and induction coil – have them checked and store them in a dry place.

Strike the mast or masts and unrig the rest of the ship. The steel wire of stays and halyards should be inspected very carefully for rust: steel wire can rust away from the inside without this being clearly

visible on the outside, usually in those places where the coating of
zinc has been damaged, for instance where there is a splice.

The spars must be carefully inspected for glued seams that have
opened and a check should be made to see that water has not pene-
trated the wood where any fittings are attached. Fittings should fit
closely against the wood, and the screws should all be tight. Before
the spars are stored they should be cleaned, scraped and given one
coat of varnish. The spars must be stored horizontally and supported
in such a way that they cannot sag.

When a wooden yacht is put ashore it should be properly supported to prevent hogging or sagging. Thus motor-yachts should be
specially supported under the engine, sailing yachts under the ballast-
keel and under bow and counter, especially if there is any substantial

Fig. 42

overhang. (Fig. 42.) It is advisable to remove loose ballast from the
vessel and to re-install it in the spring. The loose ballast in a wooden
boat should at any rate be stacked on the keel for the winter in such a
way that the hull cannot sag. If the ship is to winter out of doors it
should be placed in such a position that the deck scuppers and cockpit drains can function normally so that no water is trapped. This can
be checked with a few buckets of water. Wooden boats must be completely dry internally, because otherwise the garboard strakes may be
forced from the keel in a frost, each winter a little farther. (Fig. 43.)

Radio or other electronic equipment must not remain on board in
winter.

Woodwork that has to be completely repainted can be treated with
a paint remover and given one primer coat. Paint work below the

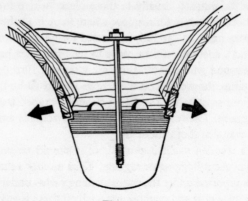

Fig. 43

water-line of a wooden boat is better left until spring, because the wood will then be drier. Painting techniques fall outside the scope of this manual but anyone who proposes to do his own painting should follow carefully the directions given for the paint he uses.

Steel-built yachts, irrespective of whether they spend the winter on shore or afloat, should be cleaned below the water-line in the autumn; the rust should be removed and they should be tarred or painted below the water-line according to previous practice. If the hull-plates show severe pitting, it is time to put on zinc anodes (see Chapter XII). Polyester yachts that have been damaged and marred by unsightly scratches can be repaired by the manufacturer. If this is not possible, and if it is desired to take some steps to improve the appearance, painting is the only solution. Ask the paint manufacturer for advice.

A very useful job to do in winter is to dismantle, clean and grease all blocks, winches and other mechanical equipment on deck. There are many advantages in doing this work oneself; it saves money, while it brings defects to light which need to be remedied. Moreover, one becomes better acquainted with the construction of the various elements, which may be very useful in the event of defects arising during the season.

Whenever a vessel is out of the water the propeller-shaft should be checked for corrosion and for excessive play. Moreover, the propeller should be checked to see that it is firmly fixed and undamaged. Adjustable-pitch propellers should be dismounted, cleaned, greased and remounted.

XI. Fitting Out

THE SENSIBLE owner makes his preparations for the next season during the previous autumn, but there are still a great many jobs that cannot be done until shortly before the beginning of the season. One of the most important parts of the programme is the checking of the engine.

If the starter motor and generator have not been removed in the autumn, the guards should be taken off in spring in order to check the brushes and commutators. The starter motor can be tried as soon as the battery is connected. When doing this, make sure that no petrol fumes are present in the engine-room. If the brushes spark excessively, the starter motor must be unshipped and sent to a specialist for repair. If the starter motor functions properly, it is sufficient to clean the commutator with a piece of cloth dipped in petrol. Be careful that all petrol has evaporated before the engine is tried again.

The same holds good for the generator. Lubrication points should be cleaned and filled with a first-quality lubricating oil. If the generator has a grease cup with felt pads, these pads should be greased with a grease having a high melting-point. Some generators have a belt drive. The belt must be inspected and the tension checked. The tension is correct if the belt between the two pulleys can be depressed up to half an inch with the thumb. The cap of the distributor should be removed and rotor and points cleaned with very fine emery paper. The points of the contact-breaker must be cleaned and, if necessary, replaced. After cleaning, these points must be carefully adjusted and the moving parts greased according to the maker's instructions. After that the ignition and timing must be checked. Then attention should be paid to the cables going from the distributor to the ignition coil and to the sparking-plugs. If the insulation of these cables is cracked or torn, the cables must be replaced. The carburettor and petrol pump must be dismantled, cleaned and checked; packings and pump diaphragm, as well as worn parts, must be replaced. Finally, the entire fuel system should be carefully examined for leaks.

The same observations apply to the starter motor and the generator of a diesel engine; the engine itself is of course different. It should be realized that the fuel pump and the injectors are the most important parts. If a diesel engine has sufficient compression and a properly working fuel system, it ought to run well. The care of the fuel system is no job for an amateur, but should be left to an expert.

All pipes leading outboard must be connected up and made tight. In order to determine whether all sea-cocks function properly, pipes can be filled with water; any leaks are then directly visible outside the vessel. It is advisable to inspect the yacht carefully for leaks immediately after launching.

Before stepping a fixed mast, the mast track should be checked by means of a spare slide. Any lights fitted on the mast and the standing and running rigging should also be checked; once the mast is stepped, it will not be so easy.

Before the boat is taken out the heads should be carefully inspected. Dismantling is necessary for cleaning, checking, replacement of the valves, if need be, and repacking of the glands.

XII. Corrosion and Rot

CORROSION

CORROSION OF the steel hull below the water-line often occurs, and it can assume dangerous proportions. The shell-plating is attacked, giving rise first to pits and eventually to large holes which may well on occasions completely penetrate the hull within a few years. Until recently it was thought that this corrosion was exclusively or mainly caused by the bronze of the propeller and that mounting-blocks of zinc in the neighbourhood of the propeller would afford a complete remedy. This supposition proved, however, to be incorrect. In the last few years various firms and shipping companies have carried out extensive tests and investigations leading to the conclusion that corrosion of hull-plates can be prevented completely or almost completely by installing anodes.

Corrosion should not be confused with the formation of rust (oxidation). An oxidizing metal combines with oxygen and forms an oxide, which, in the case of iron, is called rust. With corrosion, however, the metal slowly dissolves, leaving pits and holes in the surface. Corrosion will only take place if the water in which the metal is immersed contains an electrolyte (salt, acid or base) and hence conducts electricity. If metal is brought into an electrolyte a complex process will ensue with the result that electrically charged metal atoms (ions) are released into the electrolyte. By this process the metal is negatively charged, the liquid positively charged. This dissolution, finally resulting in the formation of pits, takes place with any metal although for precious metals it is much slower than for base metals.

It is possible to compute a table of potential (usually expressed in volts) of various metals which, in the electrolyte sea water is as follows (in order of greatest susceptibility): magnesium, zinc, iron and steel, cast iron, lead, tin, brass, copper.

If two different metals are placed in an electrolyte and are mutually connected, the more susceptible metal will dissolve and the other metal will remain unattacked.

This knowledge is applied in what is known as the cathodic protection of ships. The anode (piece of zinc or other suitable metal) dissolves, the steel hull and the bronze propeller remain completely intact.

It is advisable to have a new ship provided with adequate cathodic protection before it is launched. This can be done by mounting anodes in various places. The anodes should be specially made for the purpose; if zinc is used, it should have a high degree of purity:

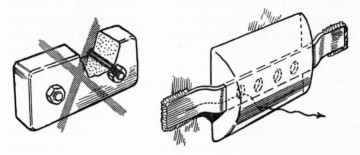

Fig. 44

the iron content should not exceed $0·0015$ per cent. Moreover, the connection between the steel and the anode material must not oxidize during the entire service life of the anode. This is achieved by casting steel retaining strips into the anode and welding them to the hull. (Fig. 44.) These anodes are available commercially. The drawback of zinc is that, as soon as it is to some extent contaminated by iron, a layer of oxide will form on the outside of the zinc, which will completely nullify its protective properties. A painted piece of zinc is also quite useless. The addition of aluminium and cadmium, however, has yielded favourable results in some cases. Magnesium, magnesium alloys and aluminium are also used for cathodic protection nowadays.

Instead of using anodes that are fixed to different points on the hull, it is also possible to protect the ship by covering her completely with a thin layer of zinc or aluminium. The layer of zinc can be applied in two ways: the ship can be painted with a zinc compound paint, or she can be sprayed with molten zinc. Aluminium is used as a compounded paint only. Prior to these treatments the steel should be cleaned and the millscale removed, by means of grit-blasting (formerly sand-blasting) or a similar method.

Severe corrosion of hull-plates will also take place when plates with residual millscale come into contact with sea water. The difference of potential between steel and millscale is very important and as wide as between steel and copper, millscale and copper being precious metals in comparison with steel. Ships that are provided with a layer of tar below the water-line will not be troubled by corrosion as long as the layer of tar forms a continuous seal, but as soon as the tar surface is damaged by a scratch, local corrosion will set in. This corrosion can only be prevented by adequate cathodic protection or by treating the whole surface with zinc.

Because of the dangers of corrosion the hull of the ship should not be used as a conductor in the electrical system. The inside of the hull will, of course, not be subject to corrosion. Here at most rust formation (oxidation) will occur and this is a very slow process. If the plates are sealed on the inside with a bituminous layer or some other air- and water-tight preservative, the iron will not rust, even though the millscale is left behind.

ROT

Wood is widely used for yacht building, indeed in many cases it is irreplaceable. The disadvantage of wood is that it may be subject to attack under certain circumstances, which will lead to the formation of rot.

Wood can only rot if the humidity in the neighbourhood of the wood is high enough to raise the moisture content of the wood to more than 20 per cent and to keep it at that level. Wet wood will only rot if it cannot dry quickly enough. Hence wood will rot less in open boats than in partly or fully decked boats.

The main causes of rot are:

1. Use of insufficiently seasoned wood.

2. Use of sap-wood. This is the young, newly formed wood, the colour of which is always different from that of the healthy, full-grown hard wood.

3. Fresh-water penetration. Salt water works as a disinfectant and prevents growth of the fungi that cause wood to rot.

The most dangerous penetration takes place along and through the deck; the water that enters the boat there is entirely fresh and moistens the deck-beams and frames while our climate seldom gives the wood an opportunity to dry out. Leaks from sink and lavatory may also be disastrous. It is therefore very important that good ventilation should be maintained to keep the air within the ship as dry as possible. Those parts of the ship that are poorly ventilated will be the first to be attacked by rot.

It is extremely difficult to establish the onset of wood rot. With boats finished in clear varnish some discoloration of the wood can usually be observed; as soon as the wood is painted, this is no longer possible. Wood rot will usually set in where fresh-water penetration occurs. These places should therefore be carefully inspected every year. Bad spots in a wooden craft must be cut out as soon as possible and replaced by sound timber. Do not be too economical when cutting out bad spots because rot spreads very rapidly, and for the best results treat the wood with a preservative. Mahogany occasionally becomes soft under water when it has been treated with bitumen. Mahogany treated with a good copper- or bronze-paint does not suffer from this disadvantage.

XIII. Sails

UNTIL RECENTLY the sails of yachts were exclusively made of cotton, Egyptian cotton being considered the best. Cotton sails have disadvantages, however: this material is very absorbent and if it is stored when still wet it is attacked by mildew – small grey mouldy spots that cannot be removed without the cloth being damaged. The strength of the cloth is, moreover, decreased by mildew.

Since 1945 nylon and other synthetic fabrics have come increasingly into use for yacht sails. Nylon has the drawback that it stretches considerably and hence is not suitable for sails that should retain a definite shape. It is only used for spinnakers, because it can be obtained in very light weights. For the other sails non-stretching, synthetic fibres, such as Terylene and Dacron, are used at present. This material is all but perfect: it has great strength, is water-repellent, water-resistant and smooth. At first these synthetic materials were expensive, but the price has gradually dropped so far that the difference in price from first-class Egyptian cotton is no longer substantial. Synthetic fibre sails can also get mildew spots; however, these spots can be removed with soap and water and a brush. Another advantage is that it does not stretch, so that the sail-maker can cut it exactly to size, which is certainly not possible with cotton. This advantage also applies when using the sail for the first time. A new cotton sail has to be treated very carefully and be stretched very slowly in a moderate breeze for it to retain its proper shape. Synthetic fibre sails can be used straightaway in all conditions.

The effect of a good sail can be largely counteracted if the sail is not properly bent and set. The luff and the foot should be stretched fairly tight until all the wrinkles in the sail have disappeared, but not tighter. In the case of gaff sails this also holds for the head. For these sails the setting of the gaff is also a very important factor. The mast track and the track on the boom – or the groove instead of a track – should be perfectly straight. If there are irregularities it will never be possible to set the sail properly. There are cases for which this is not quite true, for instance where there is a curved gaff, or where mast and boom are designed to bend during sailing. In the latter case these parts ought to be straight when not under stress.

The leech of most mainsails is cut with a roach, so that battens are necessary to keep the sail in shape. Battens are a necessary evil. Many modern materials have been tried as substitutes for old-

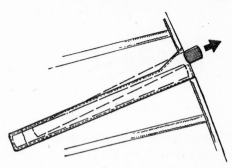

Fig. 45

fashioned ash-wood battens; whether there is a better material remains questionable however; a well-rounded and tapered ash-wood batten still causes the least wear to the sail. The batten should be a bit shorter than its pocket. Nowadays an improved design for pockets is used, making it unnecessary to secure the batten with a piece of line. (Fig. 45.)

The repair of sails is a skilled job; however, for emergency repairs one should have some limited equipment on board. Light-weight sails can be temporarily repaired with sticking-plaster. For heavier material a sail-maker's needle and yarn laid up right-handed should be used. Yarn laid up left-handed is meant for sewing-machines; it kinks when it is used for handwork. A tear in a sail should preferably be repaired with a herring-bone stitch since this stitch keeps the two parts of the cloth in the same plane. The end of the yarn is not knotted but must be fastened by the first and the last stitches. (Fig. 46.)

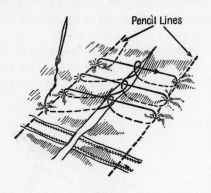

Fig. 46

Care and maintenance of the sails requires first and foremost that after the season each sail should be carefully inspected and the necessary repairs done at once. Special attention should be paid to those parts where the cloth chafes against shrouds or cross-trees. Inspection of the stitching of the seams is more important for synthetic fibre sails than for cotton ones, because in the case of synthetic fibre sails the yarn lies on the material, whereas with cotton sails the yarn tends more to bed into the sail. Sails that have been used at sea should be rinsed in fresh water in order to remove the salt. Sails in which any salt remains will not dry, so that they cannot be folded and stored.

Never wash sails in a washing-machine, and use proper soap, not synthetic detergents. A small sail can be washed in a tub; large sails should be spread out on stone in the back-yard or on a lawn and then scrubbed with a brush. The cloth should be well rinsed and be dried on a day with little wind. When the sails are thoroughly dry they must be carefully folded and stored in sail-bags. Remember that the storage space should be dry and free from mice. So never leave sails on board or in a hut, but store them at home in the attic. Sail-bags of the same material as the sails will facilitate finding the correct sail in the often overcrowded storage space on board. In this connection the application of certain colour codes to sails, sheets, blocks, halyards and shackles may be very useful.

XIV. Cordage, Bends and Hitches

ROPE USED on board ship was usually made of Manila fibres. This is a vegetable fibre originating from the Philippines and Central America. Other vegetable fibres used for making rope are: flax, sisal, hemp, coconut and cotton. The vegetable fibres all have the disadvantage that they are not rot-resistant and that the fibre does not have an unlimited length, with consequent effect on the strength of the rope.

Rope made of synthetic fibres finds increasing use; Manila, however, remains the commonest of the natural fibres in use. As Manila is not completely rot-resistant it should never be stowed away when wet. The advantages of Manila are that it can be easily spliced and knotted, it is not too smooth and has good elasticity. A long Manila hawser can sustain shocks which would have caused a steel wire of the same breaking strength to break.

Cotton rope is expensive, not strong, fairly elastic and liable to rot. However, it is soft and easy to handle and hence it is used for sheets and reef points.

Cordage made of synthetic fibres is already widely used thanks to the favourable properties of the raw materials. Nylon rope has the following important advantages over Manila:

1. It is much stronger (about twice as strong). However, wet nylon is less strong than dry nylon; the decrease in strength can be as much as 20 per cent.

2. It does not absorb water and, as a result the rope remains light and easy to handle.

3. It is highly resistant to rot.

4. It is very elastic and hence ideal for anchor and mooring ropes.

A drawback of nylon is that it is very slippery and therefore difficult to splice, knot and belay. Moreover, its high elasticity can be a serious disadvantage under certain circumstances. Rope-makers have meanwhile solved these disadvantages by putting Dacron and Terylene rope on the market. These fibres have the same advantages as nylon, but hardly stretch. By means of a special process Terylene cordage has successfully been made with a woolly surface, resembling cotton rope. This completely overcomes the drawback of this rope slipping on the cleats. One drawback still remains for all cordage made of synthetic

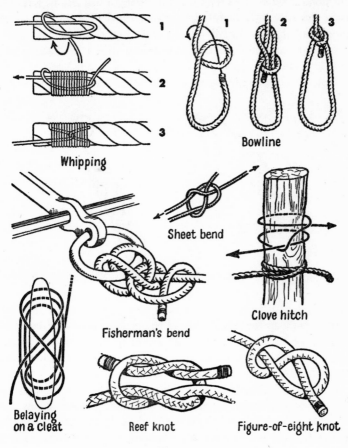

Whipping

Bowline

Sheet bend

Clove hitch

Fisherman's bend

Belaying on a cleat

Reef knot

Figure-of-eight knot

Fig. 47

fibres: the price of ropes made of synthetic fibres for any given breaking strength is still two to three times higher than that of Manila Grade I.

For rope to be reliable it should be treated properly and carefully. By coiling and uncoiling the rope the wrong way it becomes open-jawed, i.e. the number of twists per foot decreases, thereby affecting the strength of the rope. The strength will also be reduced when the rope gets more turns than normal. Therefore it is of importance that cordage be always coiled up without kinks. Rope with a right-handed lay is coiled clockwise; with a left-handed lay, anti-clockwise. (Fig. 48.)

Wear of ropes cannot always be established on the outside. For a

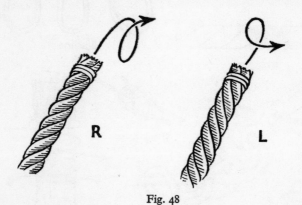

Fig. 48

proper check-up the strands should be opened a little and the heart of the rope inspected. If the fibres appear to be chafed or broken, which is clearly visible when the strands have a sharp angle on the inside, the rope should no longer be trusted.

Since Manila is not resistant to rot, it should never be used for painters or moorings. At present many impregnating agents are available which are very suitable for cordage. Synthetic cordage can always be used as a painter or for moorings. Cleats, fairleads and other parts along which the rope moves should be very smooth.

TABLE VI

CORDAGE: NOMINAL BREAKING LOAD (in lb.)

Circ. ins.	Diam. mm.	Terylene	Nylon	Manila	Cotton	Galvd. Wire 6 × 19	Galvd. Wire 1 × 19	Stainless Wire 6 × 19	Stainless Wire 1 × 19
3/8	3	200	—	—	—	1,100	1,600	1,410	1,890
1/2	4	580	650	310	140	1,800	2,500	2,110	3,250
5/8	5	850	875	—	—	2,900	3,900	2,890	5,000
3/4	6	1,200	1,250	700	450	4,300	5,600	5,080	7,600
7/8	7	1,600	1,700	—	—	5,900	7,700	6,500	9,980
1	8	2,100	2,250	1,320	780	6,700	10,000	8,100	13,300
1 1/8	9	2,600	2,800	—	—	—	—	—	—
1 1/4	10	3,200	3,500	1,740	1,230	10,500	15,600	12,550	21,000
1 1/2	12	4,500	5,000	2,630	1,760	—	—	—	—
1 3/4	14	6,100	7,000	3,530	2,400	—	—	—	—
2	16	8,000	9,000	5,000	3,140	—	—	—	—
2 1/4	18	10,000	11,200	6,000	3,580	—	—	—	—
2 1/2	20	12,300	14,000	7,900	4,400	—	—	—	—
2 3/4	22	15,000	16,800	9,350	5,360	—	—	—	—
3	24	17,900	20,200	11,200	6,400	—	—	—	—
4	32	30,000	31,200	17,100	10,900	—	—	—	—
5	40	46,000	47,500	26,200	16,200	—	—	—	—

Blocks should be suitably sized and the sheaves should be as large as possible. A safety factor of five for the use of cordage should be adhered to. This means that the normal loading should not exceed one fifth of the breaking strength given in Table VI. Sand, dirt, oil and chemicals are harmful to cordage. Ropes should be kept clean by being washed in fresh water.

Steel wire is available in numerous varieties of make and of material. Stainless steel wire is also used on board yachts, but the high price is often an objection. On an average it costs about five times as much as galvanized steel wire, while it is doubtful whether its service-life is four or five times longer. Galvanized steel wire should be inspected by inserting a marline spike between the strands, because the wire will rust sooner between the strands than on the outside. Galvanized steel wire should never be used together with stainless steel terminals because electrolysis may take place in the fittings, resulting in a very unexpected failure.

XV. Good Seamanship

GOOD SEAMANSHIP is a comprehensive term which embraces a well found ship as well as good knowledge of sailing and of the Rules of the Road. *The International Regulations for Preventing Collisions at Sea* emphasize in Rule 27 that, above all, immediate danger should be avoided. That the ship is well found and seaworthy is assumed as a matter of course after the preceding chapters. It must be emphasized that for small craft open expanses of water may be dangerous under many circumstances. Sailing an open boat such as a 12-foot dinghy in wide estuaries is possible but, in case of a sudden strong wind, very dangerous for the inexperienced. This danger is all too often underestimated. Year after year accidents happen. Unfortunately a list of craft that are, or are not, suitable for any particular area cannot be given. A competent helmsman can safely sail in an open boat, where an amateur without experience would long since have run into trouble. Here, too, it is true that making plans without knowing the weather forecast is only reckless. It should also be realized that the quality of the crew is a very important factor in the seaworthiness of a little ship. It is sometimes said of ocean-going yachts that they are only as seaworthy as their crew; this is nothing but the truth. A capable, experienced crew can ride out a gale for days in a small ship, whereas a less competent crew under the same circumstances would long since have run into difficulties through exhaustion.

A Note for Parents: Don't fuss children with a lot of directions; insist on life-jackets being worn at all times, make sure that directions about sailing in tidal waters are strictly obeyed and insist on a given time of return. If a boat does not return at the given time, then start worrying.

It goes without saying that the yacht should be fit for its purpose and should be equipped with, for instance, properly-closing hatches, a life-line round the entire ship, a self-draining cockpit, good

G

ventilation (functioning even under the most adverse circumstances), and a galley where, at all times, something hot can be prepared.

When sailing on inland waterways, or in waters such as the Thames Estuary, Southampton Water etc., it must be remembered that the waterways are meant above all for commercial shipping. A sailing or motor-yacht should not try to force a big cargo ship from her course in accordance with the regulations for preventing collision, even in instances where the yacht would be entirely within her rights to do so. Such an action would clearly be contrary to the first notions of good seamanship; it is more difficult for a big ship to alter her course than for a small yacht. Hence the main rule should always be: never obstruct merchant ships and keep to the starboard shore when this is safe and practicable. On the large rivers on the Continent the rule of keeping to the starboard side of the fairway is abrogated to meet the requirements of good seamanship – that upriver traffic follows a course where it is least inconvenienced by the current, thus always taking the inside of the bend. On the River Rhine, for instance, if a vessel is about to leave her starboard shore, a blue flag is hoisted on the bridge, or at night a white flashing light is used. For large rivers, such as the Rhine, Waal, etc., the rules of inland navigation are modified. Sailing on these waters is subject to the police regulations for sailing on the River Rhine.* These regulations are entirely adapted to the special requirements of river navigation. For many other waterways, too, special regulations are in force. Although it may be assumed that these regulations will never interfere with the rules of good seamanship, they do deviate from the rules of inland navigation.

* These regulations can be obtained in English by writing to the head office of the A.N.W.B. (the Dutch equivalent of the A.A.) in the Hague. Members of the A.A. will find the Special Services branch of that organization most helpful in obtaining information from the A.N.W.B. Similar rules obtain in Belgian, French and German waterways.

XVI. Yacht Etiquette

FLAGS

AN UNMANNED yacht at her own mooring does not wear a flag. When the yacht is actively in commission the following flags are worn:

1. *Ensign*. All British yachts may fly the Red Ensign. All *must* when entering a foreign port. Any yacht over 50 tons gross register of whatever nationality *must* wear its colours when entering or leaving a British port.

In addition to the usual Red Ensign there are in England in use in yachts the following in ascending order of importance:

  (i) Red Ensign defaced with club insignia.

 (ii) Blue Ensign defaced with club insignia.

(iii) Blue Ensign undefaced.

No one has the *right* to wear any of these three ensigns but the privilege of so doing is granted (in the case of yachts) to certain yacht clubs and can only be exercised by an individual owner in a named craft in respect of which a warrant has been granted to him personally. The special ensign can only be worn when the owner is on board or in the vicinity and must never be worn when the vessel is used commercially. At all other times the Red Ensign alone is permissible.

If a defaced ensign is worn, the burgee of the same club should be worn also.

(iv) White Ensign: to be worn only by members of the Royal Yacht Squadron.

The Union Flag is reserved for use in H.M. ships and for the use of high dignitaries. Avoid it.

Position: The Ensign, being the national flag, requires the place of honour which is the farthest possible point astern.

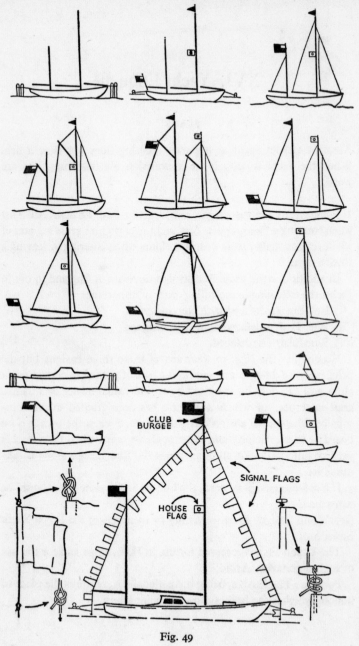

CLUB
BURGEE

SIGNAL FLAGS

HOUSE
FLAG

Fig. 49

(a) In a powered vessel this is always a flagstaff on the taffrail.

(b) In a sailing vessel a flagstaff on the taffrail is suitable in harbour but at sea it is not always feasible and in some yachts the Ensign is worn on a standing backstay unless the vessel is a gaff-rigged cutter or sloop when the Ensign is traditionally hoisted to the peak of the mainsail. In a two-masted gaff-rigged vessel under way, if an ensign staff is inconvenient, the Ensign is flown in England from the peak of the mizzen; on the Continent, from the mizzen mast-head. (This is also now considered acceptable in England.) In the case of a bermudan-rigged two-masted vessel, if an ensign staff cannot be carried at sea, the mizzen masthead is the acceptable place.

On the Continent, or in the absence of an ensign staff, motor-yachts having aft a mast with gaff also fly the Ensign at the peak of the gaff; in the case of two or more masts, at the gaff of the after-mast.

Dutch round- and flat-bottomed yachts, which are quite numerous in England, should fly the national ensign at a curved flagstaff mounted on the rudder.

An ensign is always rectangular, the length being twice the breadth. The length of an ensign should be at least 8 per cent of the length of the ship. The length of the ensign staff should be such that the ensign is well above the water.

In England 'colours' are made, that is the Ensign is hoisted, at 8 a.m. from March 25th to September 20th, at other times of year and on the Continent at 9 a.m., unless the sun rises later; in that case the flag is hoisted at sunrise. If a Royal Naval vessel is in the same port the time should be taken from her. Colours are lowered at sunset except when actually sailing in foreign territorial waters. During races the Ensign is not worn. As a sign of mourning the Ensign is worn at halfmast. British yachts should 'dip' (i.e. lower slowly two-thirds down the height of the hoist) the Ensign to a Naval vessel or to the senior Naval vessel of a squadron, whether of the Royal or other Navy, and remain dipped until similarly acknowledged. This custom is dispensed with in inland waterways.

2. *Club Burgee*. Sailing yachts fly the club burgee at the main mast-head, motor-yachts fly the burgee in the fore part of the vessel. As a rule the burgee is hoisted and lowered simultaneously with the Ensign, but it may remain hoisted during the night. The club burgee is triangular, with a ratio of 1 : 2 between hoist and length. The length of the club burgee is 4 per cent of the height of the longest mast in the case of sailing yachts, and 4 per cent of the length of the boat in the case of motor-yachts. During races the club burgee is not worn. Commodores and Vice-Commodores of English yacht clubs fly a swallow-tail pennant similar in design to a burgee but in the case of a Vice-Commodore with one ball in the upper part of the hoist, and in the case of a Rear-Commodore – if there is one – two balls in the hoist vertically above each other.

3. *House Flag*. During races, instead of and at the place of the club burgee, sailing yachts wear the house flag or a rectangular flag of any colour. Schooners wear their house flag on the main masthead during a race. The house flag is rectangular and of the same dimensions as the club burgee. It is designed by the owner himself. Apart from races, the house flag should only be worn on the Continent when the yacht is moored. In that case the flag is worn under the starboard cross-trees; with a two-masted vessel, under the cross-trees of the fore-mast; with schooners, also at the fore. In England a house flag may always be worn but it is undesirable in a vessel not racing in a place where races are being sailed. House flags may be of any design provided they do not contravene the provisions of the Merchant Shipping Act, 1894, and provided they are not so similar to another house flag as to cause confusion.

4. *Dressing Ship*. During festivities a ship that is anchored or moored may fly an ensign at each masthead, in addition to the normal flags. And a festoon of the flags of the International Code may be stretched from stem to stern via the masthead(s). If possible the square flags should alternate with pennants. The Ensign and the club burgee must project above the signal flags but the burgee must not be above the Ensign. No other flags may be flown among the signal flags.

5. *Courtesy ensigns.* In foreign waters motor- and sailing yachts wear the flag of the country they are visiting, under the starboard cross-trees or half-way up the starboard rigging of the mainmast, or half-way up the burgee halyard. When dressing ship abroad, however, the ensign of the host country is worn at the mainmast head.

Carrying other flags than those mentioned above is not correct.

GOOD MANNERS

Courtesy and good manners are at least as important as the correct flying of flags. The following actions are certainly ill-mannered.

To borrow someone else's equipment and not to return it.

To throw refuse overboard in port.

To pass moored boats at full speed.

To moor alongside a yacht without using fend-offs or using dirty fend-offs.

To walk across someone else's deck with dirty shoes, or, worse still, stiletto heels.

To walk across the after-deck of another ship. (One should always walk across the foredeck of someone else's ship when having to cross in a port.)

To be noisy at night, when other sailors want to sleep.

To be dressed like a tramp when going ashore.

To be insufficiently dressed. (Nudity is not always beautiful.)

It is impossible to give a complete list of everything in the table of seamanlike good manners. The general rule is, be courteous and helpful – and turn your radio down!

XVII. Insurance

IF ANYONE wants to find the origins of marine insurance, he will have to go back very far in history. Marine insurance began in the form of a loan given to the shipowner to be paid back with a premium once the ship had arrived safely. Nowadays many types of insurances can be effected on pleasure craft, all of them against a low premium, payable in advance.

The advantage of insurance is that underwriters are willing, against payment of a premium, to take over all the risks attendant upon sailing. Although on the face of it these risks do not seem very great, yachts burn out every year and every year serious collisions take place; the conclusion to be drawn again and again is that it is a comfort to be insured.

As regards the condition of the yacht to be insured, the underwriters depend on the utmost good faith of the assured. They assume that the ship offered to them for insurance is in good condition and is well equipped. So the duty devolves upon the owner to see that this confidence is not betrayed. Should damage appear to be the result of insufficient care, the chances are considerable that underwriters will dismiss the claim, and with good reason.

It is often argued that underwriters should have the ship inspected before it is insured. This is possible with large yachts, but for small boats it is not economically justified: the cost of an inspection by experts on shore is too high compared with the premium. It might be better to stipulate, in the same way as with sea-going vessels, that the owner must submit a certificate of seaworthiness before his ship can be insured.

It is advisable to inform underwriters as comprehensively as possible of the vessel, her equipment, and the areas to be sailed. One should also ascertain for what waters the insurance is valid.

The basic principle of insurance is the indemnification of the assured. It is a legal principle that the assured shall never make a profit out of damage. Unfortunately there are still people who are not (or do not want to be?) acquainted with this principle. Most policies for pleasure craft stipulate that payment for damage will take place after the repairs have been carried out, free from deduction for betterment of the insured vessel. Thus the cost of repairs is fully paid, up to the amount of the policy. It should be mentioned, however, that the cost of wear and tear and of damage due to wear, design or gross neglect is not made good. One should bear well in mind that certain parts of a vessel are liable to wear and tear, such as cordage, sails and tarpaulins; if a worn sail tears, it would be unfair to claim a new sail from the underwriters. What is lost is the *value* of the sail before damage not the cost of a new sail. Most English policies *exclude* damage to sails while racing unless an extra premium is paid.

As soon as a boat is insured, the owner need not concern himself with the handling of a third-party claim, or with the recovery of damage from third parties. The entire settlement of the claim is taken over by the underwriters. In Britain, the liability of insurers for third-party damage is limited by the policy. A minimum cover of £100,000 for third-party risks is advisable and not excessively expensive. In the event of collision the underwriter sees to it that an expert also examines and assesses the damage of the other party, so that afterwards no damage can be claimed that is not in any way connected with the accident. Where a vessel is insured the underwriters will also go into the question of who is liable, and will conduct civil proceedings if necessary. Should one come into collision with another vessel, the following rules must be observed:

1. If one causes damage to another vessel, all details regarding one's own identity and insurance should be given to the owner of the damaged vessel, but one should not make any admission of responsibility.
2. Always try to get the names and addresses of possible witnesses.
3. When the damage is plainly small and you are plainly at fault you can try to make a settlement on your own, but in Britain all

negotiations should be conducted 'without prejudice' so that if negotiations break down you have made no binding admissions.

4. When in doubt, ring up the underwriter. The latter can give advice himself or appoint an expert who will further deal with the matter. The cost of the call will usually be paid back by underwriters and hence need not be an objection.

Always try to make a bargain for getting the vessel off after she has run aground. If in doubt whether underwriters will accept the amount one should consult them by telephone if the vessel is not in danger. The salvors are fully entitled to retain the vessel until salvage has been paid or the payment thereof has been sufficiently guaranteed, assuming the charge is reasonable. Underwriters will be of assistance over guarantees and will provide the required amount, at any rate if the assistance rendered is not as a result of design or gross neglect on the part of the assured. If assistance is rendered without prior agreement as to charge, the salvor is entitled, as salvage, to a sum based on the value of the vessel saved, the difficulty and danger of the work and the value of his own craft.

It is unusual and unsporting of yachtsmen to claim salvage against one another unless there are special circumstances but they are entitled to do so, and some do!

For the purposes of insurance, adjustments in premium can always be obtained for changes in the risk. The three usual categories accepted by underwriters are:

(a) In commission. (Full cover within the limits of cruising ground specified.)

(b) Laid-up afloat. (Vessel will not be covered if taken from its moorings.)

(c) Laid-up ashore, the meaning of which is obvious.

Insurance on the vessel's contents and equipment will be extended free of charge to cover the storage of equipment at the yard when a boat is laid up but the policy does not cover the transport of equipment to the owner's home, nor does it cover the equipment when in his house. If expensive items of equipment are brought home for the winter they should be taken off the yacht policy and added to the contents section of the householder's fire and theft insurance policy.

Before setting out on a trip abroad one should make sure whether the insurance is valid for one's chosen cruising ground and one should ask the underwriters for the addresses of their agents, who must be called upon in the event of damage being sustained abroad.

With a good ship and good sense you should go safely to sea and safely return to land. Bon voyage!

NOTE

There are so many different kinds of yachts and motors that the advice given in this short book is of a general nature only and in any case of serious doubt or difficulty an expert should be consulted. The author and publishers regret that they cannot accept liability for any matter in connection therewith, however arising.

International Regulations for Preventing Collisions at Sea, 1948

The International Conference on the Safety of Life at Sea which was held in London in 1948 approved International Regulations for Preventing Collisions at Sea. These came into force on January 1, 1954. N.B. Paragraphs omitted here refer exclusively to seaplanes.

PART A—PRELIMINARY AND DEFINITIONS

RULE 1

(*a*) These Rules shall be followed by all vessels and seaplanes upon the high seas and in all waters connected therewith navigable by sea-going vessels, except as provided in Rule 30.

(*b*) The Rules concerning lights shall be complied with in all weathers from sunset to sunrise, and during such times no other lights shall be exhibited, except such lights as cannot be mistaken for the prescribed lights or impair their visibility or distinctive character, or interfere with the keeping of a proper look-out.

(*c*) In the following Rules, except where the context otherwise requires:

(i) the word 'vessel' includes every description of water craft, other than a seaplane on the water, used or capable of being used as a means of transportation on water;

(iii) the term 'power-driven vessel' means any vessel propelled by machinery;

(iv) every power-driven vessel which is under sail and not under power, is to be considered a sailing vessel, and every vessel under power whether under sail or not, is to be considered a power-driven vessel;

(v) a vessel or seaplane on the water is 'under way' when she is not at anchor, or made fast to the shore, or aground;

(vi) the term 'height above the hull' means height above the upper-most continuous deck;

(vii) the length and breadth of a vessel shall be deemed to be the length and breadth appearing in her certificate of registry;

(ix) the word 'visible,' when applied to lights, means visible on a dark night with a clear atmosphere;

(x) the term 'short blast' means a blast of about one second's duration;

(xi) the term 'prolonged blast' means a blast of from four to six seconds' duration;

(xii) the word 'whistle' means whistle or siren;

(xiii) the word 'tons' means gross tons.

PART B—LIGHTS AND SHAPES

RULE 2

(*a*) A power-driven vessel when under way shall carry:

(i) On or in front of the foremast, or if a vessel without a foremast then in the forepart of the vessel, a bright white light so constructed as to show an unbroken light over an arc of the horizon of 20 points of the compass (225 degrees), so fixed as to show the light 10 points ($112\frac{1}{2}$ degrees) on each side of the vessel, that is, from right ahead to 2 points ($22\frac{1}{2}$ degrees) abaft the beam on either side, and of such a character as to be visible at a distance of at least 5 miles.

(ii) Either forward of or abaft the white light mentioned in sub-section (i) a second white light similar in construction and character to that light. Vessels of less than 150 feet in length, and vessels engaged in towing, shall not be required to carry this second white light but may do so.

(iii) These two white lights shall be so placed in a line with and over the keel that one shall be at least 15 feet higher than the other and in such a position that the lower light shall be forward of the upper one. The horizontal distance between the two white lights shall be at least three times the vertical distance. The lower of these two white lights or, if only one is carried, then that light, shall be placed at a height above the hull of not less than 20 feet, and, if the breadth of the vessel exceeds 20 feet, then at a height above the hull not less than such breadth, so however that the light need not be placed at a greater height above the hull than 40 feet. In all circumstances the light or lights, as the case may be, shall be so placed as to be clear of and above all other lights and obstructing superstructures.

(iv) On the starboard side a green light so constructed as to show an unbroken light over an arc of the horizon of 10 points of the compass ($112\frac{1}{2}$ degrees), so fixed as to show the light from right ahead to 2 points ($22\frac{1}{2}$ degrees) abaft the beam on the starboard side, and of such a character as to be visible at a distance of at least 2 miles.

(v) On the port side a red light so constructed as to show an unbroken light over an arc of the horizon of 10 points of the compass ($112\frac{1}{2}$ degrees), so fixed as to show the light from right ahead to 2 points ($22\frac{1}{2}$ degrees) abaft the beam on the port side, and of such a character as to be visible at a distance of at least 2 miles.

(vi) The said green and red sidelights shall be fitted with inboard screens projecting at least 3 feet forward from the light, so as to prevent these lights from being seen across the bows.

RULE 3

(*a*) A power-driven vessel when towing or pushing another vessel or seaplane shall, in addition to her sidelights, carry two bright white lights in a vertical line one over the other, not less than 6 feet apart, and when towing more than one vessel shall carry an additional bright white light 6 feet above or below such lights, if the length of the tow, measuring from the stern of the towing vessel to the stern of the last vessel or seaplane towed, exceeds 600 feet. Each of these lights shall be of the same construction and character and one of them shall be carried in the same position as the white light mentioned in Rule 2 (*a*) (i), except the additional light, which shall be carried at a height of not less than 14 feet above the hull. In a vessel with a single mast, such lights may be carried on the mast.

(*b*) The towing vessel shall also show either the stern light specified in Rule 10 or in lieu of that light a small white light abaft the funnel or aftermast for the tow to steer by, but such light shall not be visible forward of the beam. The carriage of the white light specified in Rule 2 (*a*) (ii) is optional.

RULE 4

(*a*) A vessel which is not under command shall carry, where they can best be seen, and, if a power-driven vessel, in lieu of the lights required by Rule 2 (*a*) (i) and (ii), two red lights in a vertical line one over the other not less than 6 feet apart, and of such a character as to be visible all round the horizon at a distance of at least 2 miles. By day, she shall carry in a vertical line one over the other not less than 6 feet apart, where they can best be seen, two black balls or shapes each not less than 2 feet in diameter.

(*c*) A vessel engaged in laying or in picking up a submarine cable or navigation mark, or a vessel engaged in surveying or underwater operations when from the nature of her work she is unable to get out of the way of approaching vessels, shall carry, in lieu of the lights specified in Rule 2 (*a*) (i) and (ii), three lights in a vertical line one over the other not less than 6 feet apart. The highest and lowest of these lights shall be red, and the middle light shall be white, and they shall be of such a character as to be visible all round the horizon at a distance of at least 2 miles. By day, she shall carry in a vertical line one over the other not less than 6 feet apart, where they can best be seen, three shapes each not less than 2 feet in diameter, of which the highest and lowest shall be globular in shape and red in colour, and the middle one diamond in shape and white.

(*d*) The vessels and seaplanes referred to in this Rule, when not making way through the water, shall not carry the coloured side-lights, but when making way they shall carry them.

(*e*) The lights and shapes required to be shown by this Rule are to be taken by other vessels and seaplanes as signals that the vessel or seaplane showing them is not under command and cannot therefore get out of the way.

(*f*) These signals are not signals of vessels in distress and requiring assistance. Such signals are contained in Rule 31.

RULE 5

(*a*) A sailing vessel under way and any vessel or seaplane being towed shall carry the same lights as are prescribed by Rule 2 for a power-driven vessel or a seaplane under way, respectively, with the exception of the white lights specified therein, which they shall never carry. They shall also carry stern lights as specified in Rule 10, provided that vessels towed, except the last vessel of a tow, may carry, in lieu of such stern light, a small white light as specified in Rule 3 (*b*).

(*b*) A vessel being pushed ahead shall carry, at the forward end, on the starboard side a green light and on the port side a red light, which shall have the same characteristics as the lights described in Rule 2 (*a*) (iv) and (v) and shall be screened as provided in Rule 2 (*a*) (vi), provided that any number of vessels pushed ahead in a group shall be lighted as one vessel.

RULE 6

(*a*) In small vessels, when it is not possible on account of bad weather or other sufficient cause to fix the green and red sidelights, these lights shall be kept at hand lighted and ready for immediate use, and shall, on the approach of or to other vessels, be exhibited on their respective sides in sufficient time to prevent collision, in such manner as to make them most visible, and so that the green light shall not be seen on the port side nor the red light on the starboard side, nor, if practicable, more than 2 points (22½ degrees) abaft the beam on their respective sides.

(*b*) To make the use of these portable lights more certain and easy, the lanterns containing them shall each be painted outside with the colour of the lights they respectively contain, and shall be provided with proper screens.

RULE 7

Power-driven vessels of less than 40 tons, vessels under oars or sails of less than 20 tons, and rowing boats, when under way shall not be required to carry the lights mentioned in Rule 2, but if they do not carry them they shall be provided with the following lights:

(*a*) Power-driven vessels of less than 40 tons, except as provided in section (*b*), shall carry:

(i) In the forepart of the vessel, where it can best be seen, and at a height above the gunwale of not less than 9 feet, a bright white light constructed and fixed as prescribed in Rule 2 (*a*) (i) and of such a character as to be visible at a distance of at least 3 miles.

(ii) Green and red sidelights constructed and fixed as prescribed in Rule 2 (*a*) (iv) and (v), and of such a character as to be visible at a distance of at least 1 mile, or a combined lantern showing a green light and a red light from right ahead to 2 points (22½ degrees) abaft the beam on their respective sides. Such lantern shall be carried not less than 3 feet below the white light.

(*b*) Small power-driven boats, such as are carried by sea-going vessels, may carry the white light at a less height than 9 feet above the gunwale, but it shall be carried above the sidelights or the combined lantern mentioned in sub-section (*a*) (ii).

(*c*) Vessels of less than 20 tons, under oars or sails, except as provided in section (*d*), shall, if they do not carry the sidelights, carry where it can best be seen a lantern showing a green light on one side and a red light on the other, of such a character as to be visible at a distance of at least 1 mile, and so fixed that the green light shall not

H

be seen on the port side, nor the red light on the starboard side. Where it is not possible to fix this light, it shall be kept ready for immediate use and shall be exhibited in sufficient time to prevent collision and so that the green light shall not be seen on the port side nor the red light on the starboard side.

(*d*) Small rowing boats, whether under oars or sail, shall only be required to have ready at hand an electric torch or a lighted lantern showing a white light, which shall be exhibited in sufficient time to prevent collision.

(*e*) The vessels and boats referred to in this Rule shall not be required to carry the lights or shapes prescribed in Rules 4 (*a*) and 11 (*e*).

RULE 8

(*a*) (i) Sailing pilot-vessels, when engaged on their station on pilot-age duty and not at anchor, shall not show the lights prescribed for other vessels, but shall carry a white light at the masthead visible all round the horizon at a distance of at least 3 miles, and shall also exhibit a flare-up light or flare-up lights at short intervals, which shall never exceed 10 minutes.

(ii) On the near approach of or to other vessels they shall have their sidelights lighted ready for use and shall flash or show them at short intervals, to indicate the direction in which they are heading, but the green light shall not be shown on the port side, nor the red light on the starboard side.

(iii) A sailing pilot-vessel of such a class as to be obliged to go alongside of a vessel to put a pilot on board may show the white light instead of carrying it at the masthead and may, instead of the sidelights above mentioned, have at hand ready for use a lantern with a green glass on the one side and a red glass on the other to be used as prescribed above.

(*b*) A power-driven pilot-vessel when engaged on her station on pilotage duty and not at anchor shall, in addition to the lights and flares required for sailing pilot-vessels, carry at a distance of 8 feet below her white masthead light a red light visible all round the horizon at a distance of at least 3 miles, and also the sidelights required to be carried by vessels when under way. A bright intermittent all-round white light may be used in place of a flare.

(c) All pilot-vessels, when engaged on their stations on pilotage duty and at anchor, shall carry the lights and show the flares prescribed in sections (a) and (b), except that the sidelights shall not be shown. They shall also carry the anchor light or lights prescribed in Rule 11.

(d) All pilot-vessels, whether at anchor or not at anchor, shall, when not engaged on their stations on pilotage duty, carry the same lights as other vessels of their class and tonnage.

RULE 9

(a) Fishing vessels when not fishing shall show the lights or shapes prescribed for similar vessels of their tonnage. When fishing they shall show only the lights or shapes prescribed by this Rule, which lights or shapes, except as otherwise provided, shall be visible at a distance of at least 2 miles.

(b) Vessels fishing with trolling (towing) lines, shall show only the lights prescribed for a power-driven or sailing vessel under way as may be appropriate.

(c) Vessels fishing with nets or lines, except trolling (towing) lines, extending from the vessel not more than 500 feet horizontally into the seaway shall show, where it can best be seen, one all-round white light and in addition, on approaching or being approached by another vessel, shall show a second white light at least 6 feet below the first light and at a horizontal distance of at least 10 feet away from it (6 feet in small open boats) in the direction in which the outlying gear is attached. By day such vessels shall indicate their occupation by displaying a basket where it can best be seen; and if they have their gear out while at anchor, they shall, on the approach of other vessels, show the same signal in the direction from the anchor ball towards the net or gear.

(*d*) Vessels fishing with nets or lines, except trolling (towing) lines, extending from the vessel more than 500 feet horizontally into the seaway shall show, where they can best be seen, three white lights at least 3 feet apart in a vertical triangle visible all round the horizon. When making way through the water, such vessels shall show the proper coloured sidelights, but when not making way they shall not show them. By day they shall show a basket in the forepart of the vessel as near the stem as possible not less than 10 feet above the rail; and, in addition, where it can best be seen, one black conical shape, apex upwards. If they have their gear out while at anchor they shall, on the approach of other vessels, show the basket in the direction from the anchor ball towards the net or gear.

(*e*) Vessels when engaged in trawling, by which is meant the dragging of a dredge net or other apparatus along or near the bottom of the sea, and not at anchor:

(i) If power-driven vessels, shall carry in the same position as the white light mentioned in Rule 2 (*a*) (i) a tri-coloured lantern, so constructed and fixed as to show a white light from right ahead to 2 points (22½ degrees) on each bow, and a green light and a red light over an arc of the horizon from 2 points (22½ degrees) on each bow to 2 points (22½ degrees) abaft the beam on the starboard and port sides, respectively; and not less than 6 nor more than 12 feet below the tri-coloured lantern a white light in a lantern, so constructed as to show a clear, uniform, and unbroken light all round the horizon. They shall also show the stern light specified in Rule 10 (*a*).

(ii) If sailing vessels, shall carry a white light in a lantern so constructed as to show a clear, uniform, and unbroken light all round the horizon, and shall also, on the approach of or to other vessels show, where it can best be seen, a white flare-up light in sufficient time to prevent collision.

(iii) By day, each of the foregoing vessels shall show, where it can best be seen, a basket.

(*f*) In addition to the lights which they are by this Rule required to show, vessels fishing may, if necessary in order to attract attention of approaching vessels, show a flare-up light. They may also use working lights.

(*g*) Every vessel fishing, when at anchor, shall show the lights or shape specified in Rule 11 (*a*), (*b*) or (*c*); and shall, on the approach of another vessel or vessels, show an additional white light at least 6 feet below the forward anchor light and at a horizontal distance of at least 10 feet away from it in the direction of the outlying gear.

(*h*) If a vessel when fishing becomes fast by her gear to a rock or other obstruction she shall in daytime haul down the basket required by sections (*c*), (*d*) or (*e*) and show the signal specified in Rule 11 (*c*). By night she shall show the light or lights specified in Rule 11 (*a*) or (*b*). In fog, mist, falling snow, heavy rainstorms or any other condition similarly restricting visibility, whether by day or by night, she shall sound the signal prescribed by Rule 15 (*c*) (v), which signal shall also be used, on the near approach of another vessel, in good visibility.

NOTE. *For fog signals for fishing vessels, see Rule 15 (c) (ix).*

RULE 10

(*a*) A vessel when under way shall carry at her stern a white light, so constructed that it shall show an unbroken light over an arc of the horizon of 12 points of the compass (135 degrees), so fixed as to show the light 6 points (67½ degrees) from right aft on each side of the vessel, and of such a character as to be visible at a distance of at least 2 miles. Such light shall be carried as nearly as practicable on the same level as the sidelights.

NOTE. *For vessels engaged in towing or being towed, see Rules 3 (b) and 5.*

(*b*) In a small vessel, if it is not possible on account of bad weather or other sufficient cause for this light to be fixed, an electric torch or a lighted lantern shall be kept at hand ready for use and shall, on the approach of an overtaking vessel, be shown in sufficient time to prevent collision.

RULE II

(*a*) A vessel under 150 feet in length, when at anchor, shall carry in the forepart of the vessel, where it can best be seen, a white light in a lantern so constructed as to show a clear, uniform, and unbroken light visible all round the horizon at a distance of at least 2 miles.

(*b*) A vessel of 150 feet or upwards in length, when at anchor, shall carry in the forepart of the vessel, at a height of not less than 20 feet above the hull, one such light, and at or near the stern of the vessel and at such a height that it shall be not less than 15 feet lower than the forward light, another such light. Both these lights shall be visible all round the horizon at a distance of at least 3 miles.

(*c*) Between sunrise and sunset every vessel when at anchor shall carry in the forepart of the vessel, where it can best be seen, one black ball not less than 2 feet in diameter.

(*d*) A vessel engaged in laying or in picking up a submarine cable or navigation mark, or a vessel engaged in surveying or underwater operations, when at anchor, shall carry the lights or shapes prescribed in Rule 4 (*c*) in addition to those prescribed in the appropriate preceding sections of this Rule.

(*e*) A vessel aground shall carry by night the light or lights prescribed in sections (*a*) or (*b*) and the two red lights prescribed in Rule 4 (*a*). By day she shall carry, where they can best be seen, three black balls, each not less than 2 feet in diameter, placed in a vertical line one over the other, not less than 6 feet apart.

RULE 12

Every vessel or seaplane on the water may, if necessary in order to attract attention, in addition to the lights which she is by these Rules required to carry, show a flare-up light or use a detonating or other efficient sound signal that cannot be mistaken for any signal authorized elsewhere under these Rules.

RULE 13

(*a*) Nothing in these Rules shall interfere with the operation of any special rules made by the Government of any nation with respect to additional station and signal lights for ships of war, for vessels sailing under convoy, or for seaplanes on the water; or with the exhibition of recognition signals adopted by shipowners, which have been authorized by their respective Governments and duly registered and published.

(*b*) Whenever the Government concerned shall have determined that a naval or other military vessel or waterborne seaplane of special construction or purpose cannot comply fully with the provisions of any of these Rules with respect to the number, position, range or arc of visibility of lights or shapes, without interfering with the military function of the vessel or seaplane, such vessel or seaplane shall comply with such other provisions in regard to the number, position, range or arc of visibility of lights or shapes as her Government shall have determined to be the closest possible compliance with these Rules in respect of that vessel or seaplane.

RULE 14

A vessel proceeding under sail, when also being propelled by machinery, shall carry in the daytime forward, where it can be be seen, one black conical shape, point upwards, not less than 2 feet in diameter at its base.

RULE 15

(a) A power-driven vessel shall be provided with an efficient whistle, sounded by steam or by some substitute for steam, so placed that the sound may not be intercepted by any obstruction, and with an efficient fog-horn, to be sounded by mechanical means, and also with an efficient bell. A sailing vessel of 20 tons or upwards shall be provided with a similar fog-horn and bell.

(b) All signals prescribed by this Rule for vessels under way shall be given:
   (i) by power-driven vessels on the whistle;
   (ii) by sailing vessels on the fog-horn;
   (iii) by vessels towed on the whistle or fog-horn.

(c) In fog, mist, falling snow, heavy rainstorms, or any other condition similarly restricting visibility, whether by day or night, the signals prescribed in this Rule shall be used as follows:
   (i) A power-driven vessel making way through the water shall sound at intervals of not more than 2 minutes a prolonged blast.
   (ii) A power-driven vessel under way, but stopped and making no way through the water, shall sound at intervals of not more than 2 minutes two prolonged blasts, with an interval of about 1 second between them.
   (iii) A sailing vessel under way shall sound, at intervals of not more than 1 minute, when on the starboard tack one blast, when on the port tack two blasts in succession, and when with the wind abaft the beam three blasts in succession.
   (iv) A vessel when at anchor shall at intervals of not more than 1 minute ring the bell rapidly for about 5 seconds. In vessels of more than 350 feet in length the bell shall be sounded in the fore-part of the vessel, and in addition there shall be sounded in the after part of the vessel, at intervals of not more than 1 minute for about 5 seconds, a gong or other instrument, the tone and sounding of which cannot be confused with that of the bell. Every

vessel at anchor may in addition, in accordance with Rule 12, sound three blasts in succession, namely, one short, one pro- longed, and one short blast, to give warning of her position and of the possibility of collision to an approaching vessel.

(v) A vessel when towing, a vessel engaged in laying or in picking up a submarine cable or navigation mark, and a vessel under way which is unable to get out of the way of an approaching vessel through being not under command or unable to manœuvre as required by these Rules shall, instead of the signals prescribed in sub-sections (i), (ii) and (iii) sound, at intervals of not more than 1 minute, three blasts in succession, namely, one prolonged blast followed by two short blasts.

(vi) A vessel towed, or, if more than one vessel is towed, only the last vessel of the tow, if manned, shall, at intervals of not more than 1 minute, sound four blasts in succession, namely, one prolonged blast followed by three short blasts. When practicable, this signal shall be made immediately after the signal made by the towing vessel.

(vii) A vessel aground shall give the signal prescribed in sub-sec- tion (iv) and shall, in addition, give three separate and distinct strokes on the bell immediately before and after each such signal.

(viii) A vessel of less than 20 tons, a rowing boat, or a seaplane on the water, shall not be obliged to give the above-mentioned signals, but if she does not, she shall make some other efficient sound signal at intervals of not more than 1 minute.

(ix) A vessel when fishing, if of 20 tons or upwards, shall, at intervals of not more than 1 minute, sound a blast, such blast to be followed by ringing the bell; or she may sound, in lieu of these signals, a blast consisting of a series of several alternate notes of higher and lower pitch.

RULE 16
Speed to be moderate in fog, &c.

(a) Every vessel, or seaplane when taxi-ing on the water, shall, in fog, mist, falling snow, heavy rainstorms or any other condition similarly restricting visibility, go at a moderate speed, having careful regard to the existing circumstances and conditions.

(*b*) A power-driven vessel hearing, apparently forward of her beam, the fog-signal of a vessel the position of which is not ascertained, shall, so far as the circumstances of the case admit, stop her engines, and then navigate with caution until danger of collision is over.

PART C—STEERING AND SAILING RULES

Preliminary

1. In obeying and construing these Rules, any action taken should be positive, in ample time, and with due regard to the observance of good seamanship.

2. Risk of collision can, when circumstances permit, be ascertained by carefully watching the compass bearing of an approaching vessel. If the bearing does not appreciably change, such risk should be deemed to exist.

RULE 17

When two sailing vessels are approaching one another, so as to involve risk of collision, one of them shall keep out of the way of the other, as follows:

(*a*) A vessel which is running free shall keep out of the way of a vessel which is close-hauled.

(*b*) A vessel which is close-hauled on the port tack shall keep out of the way of a vessel which is close-hauled on the starboard tack.

(*c*) When both are running free, with the wind on different sides, the vessel which has the wind on the port side shall keep out of the way of the other.

(*d*) When both are running free, with the wind on the same side, the vessel which is to windward shall keep out of the way of the vessel which is to leeward.

(*e*) A vessel which has the wind aft shall keep out of the way of the other vessel.

RULE 18

(*a*) When two power-driven vessels are meeting end on, or nearly end on, so as to involve risk of collision, each shall alter her course to starboard, so that each may pass on the port side of the other. This Rule only applies to cases where vessels are meeting end on, or nearly end on, in such a manner as to involve risk of collision, and does not apply to two vessels which must, if both keep on their respective courses, pass clear of each other. The only cases to which it does apply are when each of two vessels is end on, or nearly end on, to the other; in other words, to cases in which, by day, each vessel sees the masts of the other in a line, or nearly in a line, with her own; and by night, to cases in which each vessel is in such a position as to see both the sidelights of the other. It does not apply, by day, to cases in which a vessel sees another ahead crossing her own course; or, by night, to cases where the red light of one vessel is opposed to the red light of the other or where the green light of one vessel is opposed to the green light of the other or where a red light without a green light or a green light without a red light is seen ahead, or where both green and red lights are seen anywhere but ahead.

RULE 19

When two power-driven vessels are crossing, so as to involve risk of collision, the vessel which has the other on her own starboard side shall keep out of the way of the other.

RULE 20

(*a*) When a power-driven vessel and a sailing vessel are proceeding in such directions as to involve a risk of collision, except as provided in Rules 24 and 26, the power-driven vessel shall keep out of the way of the sailing vessel.

RULE 21

Where by any of these Rules one of two vessels is to keep out of the way, the other shall keep her course and speed. When, from any cause, the latter vessel finds herself so close that collision cannot be avoided by the action of the giving-way vessel alone, she also shall take such action as will best aid to avert collision (see Rules 27 and 29).

RULE 22

Every vessel which is directed by these Rules to keep out of the way of another vessel shall, if the circumstances of the case admit, avoid crossing ahead of the other.

RULE 23

Every power-driven vessel which is directed by these Rules to keep out of the way of another vessel shall, on approaching her, if necessary, slacken her speed or stop or reverse.

RULE 24

(*a*) Notwithstanding anything contained in these Rules, every vessel overtaking any other shall keep out of the way of the overtaken vessel.

(*b*) Every vessel coming up with another vessel from any direction more than 2 points ($22\frac{1}{2}$ degrees) abaft her beam, i.e. in such a position, with reference to the vessel which she is overtaking, that at night she would be unable to see either of that vessel's sidelights, shall be deemed to be an overtaking vessel; and no subsequent alteration of the bearing between the two vessels shall make the overtaking vessel a crossing vessel within the meaning of the Rules, or relieve her of the duty of keeping clear of the overtaken vessel until she is finally past and clear.

(*c*) If the overtaking vessel cannot determine with certainty whether she is forward of or abaft this direction from the other vessel, she shall assume that she is an overtaking vessel and keep out of the way.

RULE 25

(*a*) In a narrow channel every power-driven vessel when proceeding along the course of the channel shall, when it is safe and practicable, keep to that side of the fairway or mid-channel which lies on the starboard side of such vessel.

(*b*) Whenever a power-driven vessel is nearing a bend in a channel where a power-driven vessel approaching from the other direction cannot be seen, such vessel, when she shall have arrived within one-half mile of the bend, shall give a signal by one prolonged blast of her whistle, which signal shall be answered by a similar blast given by any approaching power-driven vessel that may be within hearing around the bend. Regardless of whether an approaching vessel on the farther side of the bend is heard, such bend shall be rounded with alertness and caution.

RULE 26

All vessels not engaged in fishing shall, when under way, keep out of the way of any vessels fishing with nets or lines or trawls. This Rule shall not give to any vessel engaged in fishing the right of obstructing a fairway used by vessels other than fishing vessels.

RULE 27

In obeying and construing these Rules due regard shall be had to all dangers of navigation and collision, and to any special circumstances, including the limitations of the craft involved, which may render a departure from the above Rules necessary in order to avoid immediate danger.

PART D – MISCELLANEOUS

RULE 28

(*a*) When vessels are in sight of one another, a power-driven vessel under way, in taking any course authorized or required by these Rules, shall indicate that course by the following signals on her whistle, namely:

One short blast to mean 'I am altering my course to starboard.'
Two short blasts to mean 'I am altering my course to port.'
Three short blasts to mean 'My engines are going astern.'

(*b*) Whenever a power-driven vessel which, under these Rules, is to keep her course and speed, is in sight of another vessel and is in doubt whether sufficient action is being taken by the other vessel to avert collision, she may indicate such doubt by giving at least five short and rapid blasts on the whistle. The giving of such a signal shall not relieve a vessel of her obligations under Rules 27 and 29 or any other Rule, or of her duty to indicate any action taken under these Rules by giving the appropriate sound signals laid down in this Rule.

(*c*) Nothing in these Rules shall interfere with the operation of any special rules made by the Government of any nation with respect to the use of additional whistle signals between ships of war or vessels sailing under convoy.

RULE 29

Nothing in these Rules shall exonerate any vessel, or the owner, master or crew thereof, from the consequences of any neglect to carry lights or signals, or of any neglect to keep a proper look-out, or of the neglect of any precaution which may be required by the ordinary practice of seamen, or by the special circumstances of the case.

RULE 30

Reservation of Rules for Harbours and Inland Navigation

Nothing in these Rules shall interfere with the operation of a special rule duly made by local authority relative to the navigation of any harbour, river, lake, or inland water, including a reserved seaplane area.

RULE 31

Distress Signals

When a vessel or seaplane on the water is in distress and requires assistance from other vessels or from the shore, the following shall be the signals to be used or displayed by her, either together or separately, namely:

(*a*) A gun or other explosive signal fired at intervals of about a minute.

(*b*) A continuous sounding with any fog-signal apparatus.

(*c*) Rockets or shells, throwing red stars fired one at a time at short intervals.

(*d*) A signal made by radiotelegraphy or by any other signalling method consisting of the group · · · — — — · · · in the Morse Code.

(*e*) A signal sent by radiotelephony consisting of the spoken word 'Mayday'.

(*f*) The International Code Signal of distress, indicated by N.C.

(*g*) A signal consisting of a square flag having above or below it a ball or anything resembling a ball.

(*h*) Flames on the vessel (as from a burning tar barrel, oil barrel, &c.).

(*i*) A rocket parachute flare showing a red light.

The use of any of the above signals, except for the purpose of indicating that a vessel or a seaplane is in distress, and the use of any signals which may be confused with any of the above signals, is prohibited.

NOTE. *A radio signal has been provided for use by vessels in distress for the purpose of actuating the auto-alarms of other vessels and thus securing attention to distress calls or messages. The signal consists of a series of twelve dashes, sent in 1 minute, the duration of each dash being 4 seconds, and the duration of the interval between two consecutive dashes 1 second.*

RULE 32

All orders to helmsmen shall be given in the following sense: right rudder or starboard to mean 'put the vessel's rudder to starboard'; left rudder or port to mean 'put the vessel's rudder to port.'